Sc1 skills
for Key Stage 3

Chris Tooley

PEARSON
Longman

Pearson Education Limited
Edinburgh Gate
Harlow, Essex CM20 2JE, England
and Associated Companies throughout the World

Second impression 2005
ISBN 0 582 83120 2

Designed by Gemini Design, Hersham, Surrey

Printed in China
NPCC/02

The publisher's policy is to use paper manufactured from sustainable forests.

About the author

Chris Tooley is an Assistant Principal working at Soham Village College, a secondary school in the Cambridgeshire Fens. He is also an Advanced Skills Teacher (AST). Much of Chris' work as an AST has centred on supporting teachers in Cambridgeshire to deliver the skills of scientific enquiry (Sc1). This has involved producing materials, providing INSET and working as a Leading Science Teacher.

Acknowledgements

The author and publisher would like to thank the following for their help during preparation of Sc1 skills for Key Stage 3:

Joanna Tooley, advice on development and shaping of the materials, particularly the thinking skills sections.

Manuscript Advice

Alastair Sandiforth, Head of Sciences, Stanborough School, Welwyn Garden City

Advice on National Curriculum Levels in assessment materials

Dr Colin McCarty

CONTENTS

CONTENTS

Sc1 Skills for Key Stage 3 © Pearson Education Limited 2004

INTRODUCTION

Background

The inception of the Key Stage 3 strategy, with its focus on a three-part lesson, and the move by the Qualifications and Curriculum Authority (QCA) to increase the focus of the KS3 National Curriculum assessments on Sc1 (Scientific Enquiry), created the momentum behind the production of these materials. The two main aims for these materials are outlined below:

To develop a deeper understanding of Sc1 skills

Pupils' understanding is developed through the medium of starter sessions, a pupil booklet and SAT style questions. In this way pupils' understanding of investigative skills are developed as well as serving as a thorough preparation for end of key stage assessments.

To be flexible and easy to develop and use

All materials are produced in a form allowing them to be photocopied on to paper or overhead transparencies, or for use with a digital projector. They are all easily adaptable using standard word processing and presentation packages, allowing you to customise them to suit the needs of your pupils. A series of simple templates has also been prepared to allow teachers to create their own bank of personalised and professional resources.

The components

Starters

Five starters are provided for each QCA unit for years 7 and 8 with three for each unit in year 9. These reflect the content of the QCA units for each year group and show a progression of difficulty and skills development throughout the key stage. This is shown on the skills progression chart on page vii.

Additionally, starters based around thinking skills have been developed for each QCA unit. These take the form of a graph or table reflecting the content of the unit. The thinking skills starters encourage pupils to reflect on the questions they should be asking when carrying out investigations. Pupils are then asked to devise their own questions that could be asked of the given data. These questions can then be swapped with other members of the class and completed immediately or used at the end of the teaching session as a plenary exercise.

Should teachers wish to focus upon a particular strand of science (Sc2, 3 or 4) or Sc1 skill area, they can search for appropriate starters using the table on page ix. All starters can be used by photocopying the printed versions on to paper or overhead transparencies, or alternatively a direct projection system could be used. Starter activities on the CD Rom are in two editable formats, Word and PowerPoint®, so that they can be adapted to suit specific classes, levels or contexts before being presented to the class. The addition of response lines enables pupils to note down their ideas should they wish to.

Answers are provided for each starter question in both the printed resource and on the CD Rom, along with suggestions of extension activities. Additionally, where appropriate, starters show links to specific sections of *Exploring Science* allowing the most appropriate starters to be selected to complement the lesson content.

Starter templates

Template files have been produced which allow teachers to easily develop their own bank of customised resources if they have a version of PowerPoint®. There are 12 different template files covering the following areas:

Planning	Obtaining	Analysing	Evaluating
identifying variables	producing tables	interpreting tables	lines of best fit and anomalies
predictions	presenting results as graphs	interpreting line graphs	evaluating investigations
fair tests		interpreting bar graphs	
planning		forming conclusions	

Each template comprises two types of page.

Presentation page

This page represents the template on which starter sessions can be developed, saved and subsequently printed/projected. The page has two areas. One is dedicated to setting a context on which subsequent questions are based and the other is for the insertion of the questions themselves.

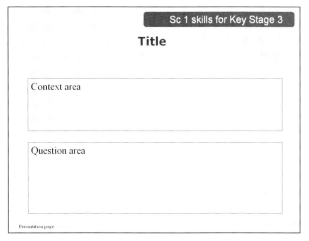

The content of both of these areas is composed using the resource pages.

Resource pages

These pages contain two types of resource:

- standard questions
- standard images (e.g. tables, graph outlines).

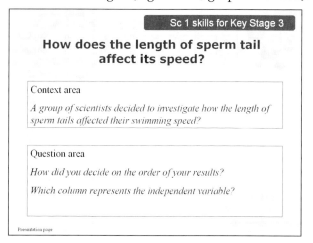

Each type of object can easily be copied and pasted into the context and question areas of the presentation page to quickly build up a new customised starter. Extra text can then be entered. Custom designed graphs can also be added at this time. This file can then be saved for further amendment as required.

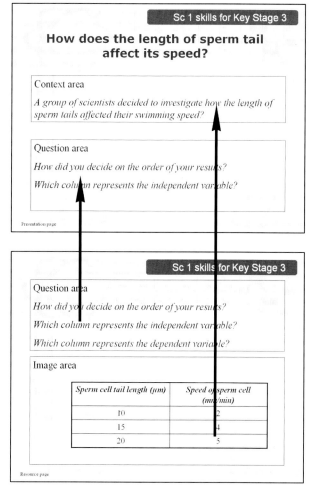

Alternatively, versions of the templates are included in Word format on the CD Rom, allowing questions to be inserted, edited and saved as required.

SATs Questions

Twenty SAT style questions have been developed around the context of Sc1 reflecting the increased emphasis on questions testing investigative skills in National Curriculum assessments. These materials are intended for use as starter/plenary exercises throughout year 9 at an appropriate point in relation to skills or content development. However, an alternative would be to use them in the lead up to the examinations themselves. The exercises are drawn from across the three key stage 3 science curriculum ranges, spanning levels 3 to 7. The SAT question chart (page viii) can be used to select questions focusing on specific skills, levels or strands. The questions reflect the level at which skills are introduced to pupils.

Once again, full answers are provided and can be photocopied onto paper, overhead transparencies or presented using a direct projection system. All are fully editable using standard word processor or presentation packages.

Pupil booklet

In addition, a booklet has been designed to provide pupils with a central location on which to build understanding of each aspect of Sc1. It can be used for reference when carrying out practical investigations and also contains sections where pupils can make their own notes and reminders.

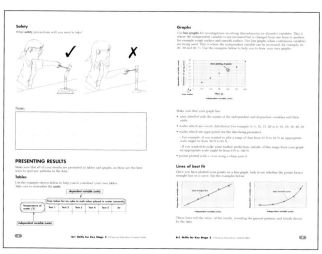

This resource is available in printed format and also as an editable file on the CD Rom. It can be printed or photocopied double sided and then put together to form a 12-page A4-sized booklet as shown below:

Photocopy pages 12 + 1, 10 + 3, 8 + 5 as A3 pages. Then photocopy the matching pairs on the reverse. Fold the three A3 sheets and collate into correct page order.

page 12	page 1	page 10	page 3	page 8	page 5
page 11	page 2	page 9	page 4	page 7	page 6

SKILLS PROGRESSION CHART

Planning	Variables and forming questions	Predictions	Planning – fair investigations, range and repetitions	Planning – equipment and accuracy
YEAR 7	Understand and use the terms, independent, dependent and control variable. Form an investigative question by identifying the range of possible variables.	Form predictions with discrete and continuous variables informed by everyday experience or simple scientific knowledge.	Identify the necessary variables which need to be controlled to make an investigation fair. Understand and explain the need for a control in investigations. Repeat readings and explain why repetition is needed.	Select appropriate equipment to measure variables. Include safety in all plans.
YEAR 8	Independently form a question involving the use of discrete and/or continuous variables.	Form predictions with discrete and continuous variables informed by scientific knowledge and understanding.	Identify when ranges are unsuitable in investigative procedures.	Select equipment with discrimination to gain the most accurate readings.
YEAR 9		Use data from a table or graph to make predictions.	Suggest suitable ranges for the independent variable.	Select equipment with fine discrimination to gain the most accurate readings – including data loggers.

Presenting/ interpreting	Producing tables	Producing graphs	Interpreting tables	Interpreting graphs
YEAR 7	Design appropriate tables for values of an independent variable and a dependent variable.	Plot bar and line graphs, making informed decisions on the positions of the independent and dependent variables.	Identify the independent and dependent variables and pick out specific values (e.g. maximum and minimum).	Identify the independent and dependent variables.
YEAR 8	Design tables for series of data including the calculation of averages.	Select the type of graph and scale appropriate to the task at hand. Draw lines of best fit onto plotted points.	Identify anomalous results and provide explanations for their occurrence. Identify independent and dependent variables.	Take readings from graphs, including making predictions of intermediate values. Identify independent and dependent variables.
YEAR 9	Design complex tables including the calculation of averages.	Explain why a particular type of graph/scale is appropriate for specific circumstances.		Describe patterns found in results and identify where variables are changing most rapidly.

Concluding/ evaluating	Lines of best fit/anomalies	Pattern identification/ description	Conclusions	Evaluations
YEAR 7		Describe the relationship between continuous relationships.	Explain the findings of investigations using simple scientific knowledge and understanding.	Judge the fairness of an investigation, making recommendations for improvements.
YEAR 8	Identify anomalous results in tables and graphs drawn with lines of best fit. Suggest reasons for anomalies.		Explain the findings of investigations using detailed scientific knowledge and understanding.	Judge the accuracy of investigative techniques and make suggestions for improvements.
YEAR 9	Draw lines of best fit (straight lines and best curves) onto plotted points and use these to identify anomalous results.		Compare the findings of investigations with predictions.	Judge whether data is sufficient to form a firm conclusion.

SAT QUESTION CHART

Skill		Level				
		3	4	5	6	7
Variables and forming questions	Sc2		3			
	Sc3		4, 19			
	Sc4		12	16		
Predictions	Sc2		7	1		
	Sc3					5, 8, 13
	Sc4			14	10	12
Planning – fair test	Sc2	21, 23	1, 3, 7			
	Sc3	22	4, 19			
	Sc4		17			
Planning – repetition and range	Sc2			18		
	Sc3			4, 11, 19	20	
	Sc4					
Planning – equipment, precision and safety	Sc2	18, 21				
	Sc3	2	2	2		
	Sc4	14, 17				
Producing tables	Sc2	21	11			
	Sc3					
	Sc4		14			
Producing line graphs	Sc2					
	Sc3			8, 13		
	Sc4					
Interpreting tables	Sc2	11		1		
	Sc3					
	Sc4					
Interpreting graphs	Sc2		15	15		
	Sc3		2			
	Sc4					
Lines of best fit/ anomalies	Sc2					
	Sc3			20	5, 20	5, 13
	Sc4				6	6, 8, 12
Pattern identification/ description	Sc2		1			
	Sc3		20, 22			
	Sc4		6, 12			
Conclusions	Sc2			15	7	3, 15
	Sc3		22			
	Sc4		16	10	16, 17	9
Evaluations	Sc2	23	18		7	
	Sc3			2		
	Sc4				9	

SKILLS INDEX

Skill	Strand context	Year 7	Year 8	Year 9
Variables and forming questions	Sc2	A2 B1 B2 C3 C4 D4 D5	A2 A5 B4 C1 D3	A1 A2 C1 D1
	Sc3	F1 F4 F5 G1 G3 G5 H1 H5	F1 F4 G5	E1 E2 F1
	Sc4	I2 I4 J1 J5 K1	J1 J2 J3 K3, K4, L1 L5	I1
Predictions	Sc2	B4 C1 C4	A1 B2, B4 C1 C4 C5	A2 C1 D1
	Sc3	E4 G2 H2 H3 H5	E3 F4 G2 G3 G4 H1	E3 G2
	Sc4	I4 J2 K1 K2 K3 L2 L3 L4 L5	I4 K5 L1 L3 L5	J1 J2 J3 L1 L2 L3
Planning – fair test	Sc2	A3 C3 C4 D2 D3 D4	A5 C1 D4	A2 B1 C2
	Sc3	E1 F4 G3	E1 G1 G2 H1 H3	E1 F1 F2 H1
	Sc4	I1 J4 K2	I1	K1
Planning – repetition and range	Sc2	A2 A3 A4 C2 C5 D2	A3 D3 D4	C2 C3
	Sc3	F4 H4	F5 G1 G3 H3	F2 H2 H3
	Sc4	J4	I2 L2	I2 K1
Planning – equipment, precision and safety	Sc2	A1 A3 C2 C5	C4 D4 D5	A1
	Sc3	E1 E2 E5 F1 G1 H4	E3 E4 G1 H3 H4 H5 D4	E1 F2 H1
	Sc4	I1 I2 J1 J4 K3	I1 I2 I5 K4 L1	I1 K1
Producing tables	Sc2	B4 D1	B4 D1 D4	A3 B3
	Sc3	E2 F2	H2	F3
	Sc4	K1	I5 J5 K2	K2
Producing graphs	Sc2	B5 C2	A4 B1 B4 C3 D4	A3 D1
	Sc3	F3	H2 H4	H3
	Sc4		J4 K1 K4 L3	I3 J3 L3
Interpreting tables	Sc2	A4 B1 B5 C5 D1		
	Sc3	E3 E4 H2	E2 E4 E5 H2 H4	G3
	Sc4		J1 J5	J1 K2
Interpreting graphs	Sc2	A5 B3	A1 B1 B5 C2 C5 D2	B1 D1
	Sc3	F5 H1	F2 F3 G4 G5	E3 G1
	Sc4	I3 I5 K4 L5	L4	
Lines of best fit/anomalies	Sc2		A3 C5	C3 D3
	Sc3		F1 F3 F5 G4	E2 H3
	Sc4		J3 L3	I3
Pattern identification/description	Sc2	B1 B2 B4 D1 D4	A2 D2	A3 B2 B3 D2 D3
	Sc3	E4 F2 F5 G5 H5	F4 H5	E3 F3 G1
	Sc4	I5 J1 J3 K5 L1 L4	I3 I4 J4 K3 L3 L5	I3 J1 J2 L1 L3
Conclusions	Sc2		B1 B5 C2 C4 D2	B2 D2 D3
	Sc3	E5 F2 F3	E4 F2	G1 G2
	Sc4	I5 J3 J5 K5 L1 L3 L5	I4 K2	
Evaluations	Sc2	D3	A3 B2 B3	B1
	Sc3	G4 E3	E1 E4 F5 G2	G3 H2
	Sc4	I2	I2 K2 L4	K2 K3

STARTER WORKSHEET

1 Looking at plant cells

Sam wanted to look at some plant cells.
He was given a magnifying glass and
a microscope to choose from.
Sam chose the microscope.

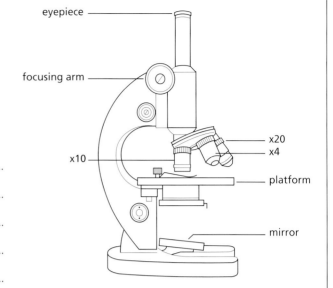

a Why did Sam choose the microscope?

....

....

....

....

....

Sam then took some onion skin and placed it on a microscope slide.
He had to choose the right objective lens (magnification) for the microscope.
His microscope had three choices:

×4, ×10 and ×20.

b Which lens should Sam use when first looking at the cells?

....

c Explain your answer to part (b).

....

....

Sam selected the correct lens and then looked down his microscope.
All he saw was a very dim image.

Look at the diagram on the right showing how the equipment was set up.

d Can you explain why Sam couldn't see the image clearly?

....

....

....

....

....

....

....

....

....

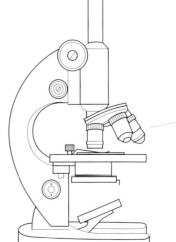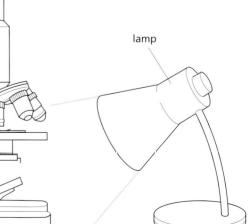

Link – Exploring Science 7Aa

STARTER WORKSHEET

2 Investigating pollen tube growth

Katie and Roisin wanted to find out what effect the variable – concentration of sugar solution, would have on another variable – the length that pollen tubes grew.

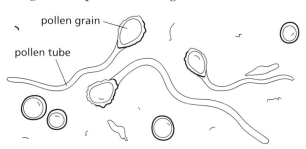

a In Katie and Roisin's investigation, name:

  i the independent variable

  ....

  ....

  ii the dependent variable.

  ....

Katie decided that they should use the following range of sugar concentrations in the investigation: 5%, 10%, 15%, 25%, 30%, 35% and 40%.

Roisin said that this range was not ideal.

b What do you think is wrong with this range?

  ....

Link – Exploring Science 7Ae

Sc1 Skills for Key Stage 3 © Pearson Education Limited 2004

✂ ....

STARTER WORKSHEET

3 Investigating pollen tube growth

Katie and Roisin decided to find out what effect the concentration of sugar solution would have on the length that pollen tubes grew. The investigation was done at room temperature (approximately 21 °C). Katie and Roisin decided on a suitable range of sugar concentrations to use and repeated the investigation five times.

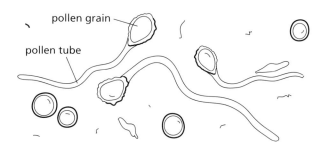

a Why did Katie and Roisin repeat the investigation?

  ....

b What variables would Katie and Roisin have to keep the same?

  ....

c Why was it important to keep these the same?

  ....

d What units should be used to measure the pollen tubes?

  ....

Link – Exploring Science 7Ae

 Sc1 Skills for Key Stage 3 © Pearson Education Limited 2004

STARTER WORKSHEET

4 Investigating pollen tube growth

Katie and Roisin decided to find out what effect the concentration of sugar solution would have on the length that pollen tubes grew. Their results are shown in the table below:

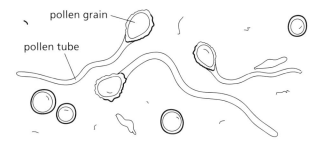

pollen grain

pollen tube

Concentration of sugar solution (%)	Average length of pollen tube (mm)
5	2
10	4
15	7
20	8
25	11
30	15
35	12
40	7

a At which concentration did the pollen tubes grow best? ....

Katie and Roisin's teacher said that these results were not enough to say which concentration of sugar produced the most growth.

b What should Katie and Roisen do to be certain of their conclusion?

....

....

....

c How would these results best be displayed?

....

....

d What do you think the average length of the pollen tube would be if the sugar solution had a concentration of 45%?

....

Link – Exploring Science 7Ae

STARTER WORKSHEET

5 Investigating pollen tube growth

Katie and Roisin decided to find out what effect the concentration of sugar solution would have on the length that pollen tubes grew. Here is a graph of their results:

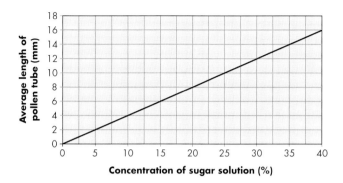

a Use the graph to help you identify:

    i the independent variable

    ....

    ii the dependent variable.

    ....

b Use the graph to help you with these questions:

    i What might the average length of a pollen tube grown in a 5% sugar solution be?

    ....

    ii What concentration of sugar solution might produce an average pollen tube length of 10 mm?

    ....

c What piece of equipment would be needed to precisely measure the length of pollen tubes?

....

d Suggest an appropriate title for the graph.

....

....

Link – Exploring Science 7Ae

Sc1 Skills for Key Stage 3 © Pearson Education Limited 2004

STARTER WORKSHEET

1 **How does the length of a sperm tail affect its speed?**

A group of scientists decided to investigate how the length of sperm tails affected their swimming speed.

Here are their results:

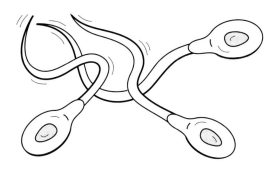

Sperm cell tail length (µm)	Speed of sperm cell (mm/min)
10	2
15	4
20	5

a Look at the results in the table and use them to name:

i the independent variable ....

ii the dependent variable. ....

b Describe the relationship between tail length and speed.

....

....

Link – Exploring Science 7Bb

Sc1 Skills for Key Stage 3 © Pearson Education Limited 2004

STARTER WORKSHEET

2 **Does smoking during pregnancy affect babies' birth weight?**

A group of scientists wanted to find out how babies' birth weight might be affected by the number of cigarettes their mothers smoked per day. On the right is a bar chart of their results:

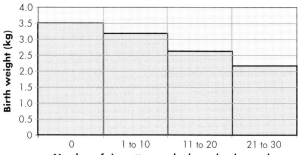

a How did the number of cigarettes smoked per day affect the birth weight?

....

....

A large cigarette firm argued that this was not a fair test because there were lots of other factors that could have affected birth weight.

b Suggest some other variables which could have affected the babies' birth weights.

....

....

Link – Exploring Science 7Bd

Sc1 Skills for Key Stage 3 © Pearson Education Limited 2004

STARTER WORKSHEET

3   Investigating the growth of a fetus

The graph shows how the length of a fetus changes over the 40 weeks of pregnancy.

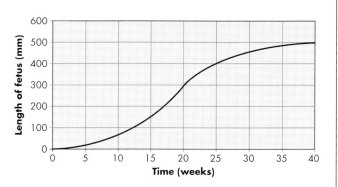

a From the graph, work out:

   i the length of the fetus at 20 weeks

   ....

   ii how old the fetus is when it is 400 mm in length

   ....

   iii when the fetus was growing at the fastest rate.
   Was the fastest rate between 5 and 10 weeks, 10 and 15 weeks, or 15 and 20 weeks?

   ....

b How did you work out your answer to (aiii)?

....

Link – Exploring Science 7Bd

Sc1 Skills for Key Stage 3 © Pearson Education Limited 2004

STARTER WORKSHEET

4   Are length and width of feet related?

A class decided to find out whether there was a relationship between the width and length of their feet. Four pupils were selected and their feet measured. The results were put into a table.

Pupils' names	Foot width (cm)	Foot length
Angela	5	14
Joanna	6	16
Eammon	8	21
Ash	9	23

a What information is missing from the table?

....

b Describe the relationship between the width of the pupils' feet and their length.

....

c Sarah has feet which measure 7 cm in width. Using the information in the table, can you predict how long Sarah's feet are likely to be?

....

Sc1 Skills for Key Stage 3 © Pearson Education Limited 2004

STARTER WORKSHEET

5 Investigating height in girls and boys

The table shows how the average height of girls and boys changes as they get older.

Age	Average height of girls (cm)	Average height of boys (cm)
9	140	140
10	145	143
11	155	147
12	163	155
13	165	166
14	167	175
15	168	177

a What is the average height of boys when they are 12 years old? ....

b When is the average girl taller than the average boy? ....

c Can you suggest a better way of presenting this information than in a table?

....

....

Link – Exploring Science 7Be

Sc1 Skills for Key Stage 3 © Pearson Education Limited 2004

✂

UNIT 7B **REPRODUCTION**

STARTER WORKSHEET

5 Investigating height in girls and boys

The table shows how the average height of girls and boys changes as they get older.

Age	Average height of girls (cm)	Average height of boys (cm)
9	140	140
10	145	143
11	155	147
12	163	155
13	165	166
14	167	175
15	168	177

a What is the average height of boys when they are 12 years old? ....

b When is the average girl taller than the average boy? ....

c Can you suggest a better way of presenting this information than in a table?

....

....

Link – Exploring Science 7Be

Sc1 Skills for Key Stage 3 © Pearson Education Limited 2004

STARTER WORKSHEET

1 What happens to environmental conditions in a classroom?

Mario and Jacinta are going to study how some environmental conditions in their classroom change over an 18 hour period from 3 pm, through the night until 9 am the next morning. They choose to measure temperature, light intensity and noise levels.

Predict what you think will happen to each of these factors from 3 pm until midnight by choosing the correct words from the options given, and then explain why you think this will happen:

a The temperature will ☐ increase ☐ decrease ☐ stay the same

because ....

b The light intensity will ☐ increase ☐ decrease ☐ stay the same

because ....

c The noise levels will ☐ increase ☐ decrease ☐ stay the same

because ....

Link – Exploring Science 7Ca

STARTER WORKSHEET

2 What happens to environmental conditions in a classroom?

Mario and Jacinta are studying how some environmental conditions in their classroom change over an 18 hour period from 3 pm, through the night until 9 am the next morning.

They plan to measure the temperature of the classroom.

a What piece of equipment could they use to measure and record the temperature change in the classroom during their investigation?

....

Mario and Jacinta set up their equipment and left it running overnight. The next morning they collected their data and presented it to the class.

b What would be the best way to present the data for the class to see?

....

Mario decided that he wanted to repeat the experiment the following night. Jacinta said that this wasn't worth doing as it would give exactly the same results.

c Do you think that repeating the experiment would give exactly the same results? Explain your answer.

....

....

....

....

Link – Exploring Science 7Ca

STARTER WORKSHEET

3 How do environmental conditions affect woodlice?

Woodlice like to live underneath old logs or rocks and are rarely found in dry places. Class 7A wanted to investigate how the conditions in an environment affect woodlice.

a What range of conditions (variables) could pupils investigate?

....

....

....

....

....

b Choose one variable and design a simple plan to investigate it. Make sure that you mention how many woodlice you will use, the variables that you will control and those which you will measure. Include diagrams of any apparatus you will use.

....

....

....

....

....

....

....

....

....

....

Link – Exploring Science 7Cc

Sc1 Skills for Key Stage 3 © Pearson Education Limited 2004

STARTER WORKSHEET

4 Why do rabbits have thicker fur in winter?

Arwen and Howard noticed that their pet rabbit had thicker fur in the winter than in the summer. Arwen thought that this was to do with keeping warm. They decided to investigate whether the change in fur was linked to keeping warm.

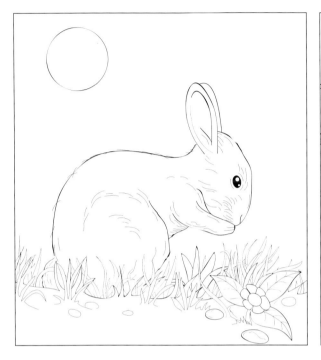 

They took three tin cans. They wrapped one in three layers of cotton wool, one in a single layer and left one with no cotton wool at all. They then filled each can with hot water and measured the temperature change of the water over the next 10 minutes.

a What is being investigated here? Complete the sentence below:

What affect does the ....

have on the .... ?

b What variables would Arwen and Howard have to keep the same to make the investigation fair?

....

....

....

c Predict which can would keep the water hottest.

....

d Explain your prediction.

....

....

Link – Exploring Science 7Cb

STARTER WORKSHEET

5 **Why do rabbits have thicker fur in winter?**

Arwen and Howard noticed that their pet rabbit had thicker fur in the winter than in the summer. Arwen thought that this was to do with keeping warm. They decided to investigate whether the change in fur was linked to keeping warm.

First they wrapped different amounts of cotton wool around some identical tin cans and filled each with 100 cm³ of water at 60 °C. After 10 minutes they measured the temperature of the water in each can. Here are their results:

Temperature	No covering	One layer of cotton wool	Three layers of cotton wool
at start	60 °C	60 °C	60 °C
after 10 mins	35 °C	44 °C	56 °C

a Explain why the can with no covering was used in this investigation.

....

....

b Which can was the best at keeping the water warm?

....

Arwen and Howard measured the temperature of the water in the cans with laboratory thermometers.

c What would be a more precise way of measuring temperature?

....

d Suggest another improvement to the experiment.

....

....

....

Link – Exploring Science 7Cb

Sc1 Skills for Key Stage 3 © Pearson Education Limited 2004

STARTER WORKSHEET

1 Do longer holly leaves have more prickles?

Gerda wanted to see if the length of a holly leaf affected the number of prickles that it had.

She looked at five leaves. Here are her results:

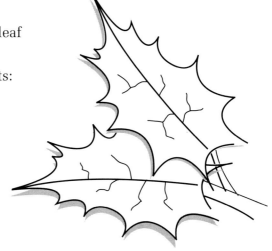

5.0 cm – 13 prickles

3.5 cm – 5 prickles

4.5 cm – 11 prickles

4.0 cm – 9 prickles

3.0 cm – 7 prickles

a Record the results in a table:

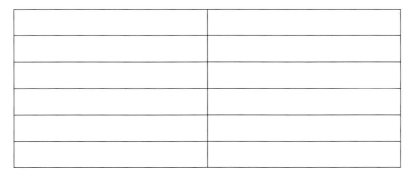

Gerda looked at the results and said that she could see a pattern.

b Describe the pattern that Gerda saw in her results.

....

....

....

....

....

c Gerda's teacher said that she needed to collect more data if she wanted to be sure her pattern was reliable. Explain why this is true.

....

....

....

Link – Exploring Science 7Da

STARTER WORKSHEET

2 Which fertilisers are best for grass?

David wanted to find out which fertilisers made grass grow tallest. He decided to investigate four areas of grass on the school field which had just been cut to the same height. The picture below shows his results, with the names of the fertilisers he added to each section.

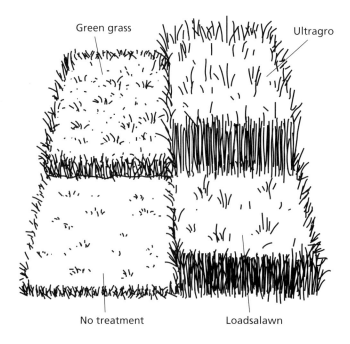

At the end of 2 weeks, David planned to measure the height of 20 blades of grass in each area and calculate their average height.

a Which things would David have to keep the same to make the investigation fair?

....

....

....

b Why was some ground left without any fertiliser?

....

....

....

Sandy said that measuring the average height of the grass might not show which fertiliser had caused the most growth. He suggested that the average mass would be better for this purpose.

c How would you measure the mass of 20 blades of grass?

....

Link – Exploring Science 7Db

STARTER WORKSHEET

3 How does light affect plant growth?

Amil wanted to find out how the amount of light affected plant growth. He took three young sunflower plants and grew them in the following conditions:

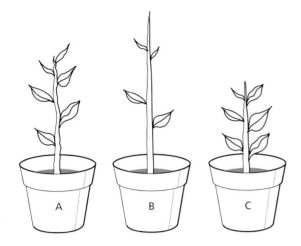

- A – In bright light, warmth and with plenty of water.
- B – In the dark, warmth and with plenty of water.
- C – In bright light, cold and with no water.

At the end of 5 days Amil measured the heights of each sunflower. He found that plant B had grown the highest. Amil thought this meant that plants grow better in the dark than in the light.

Jacqueline said that Amil's investigation was not fair.

a Explain why you think that Amil's investigation was not fair.

....

....

b Suggest how Amil could have set up his investigation to make it fair.

....

....

c Explain why plants put all their efforts into growing upwards when they are shaded.

....

....

Link – Exploring Science 7Db

STARTER WORKSHEET

4 How do different amounts of water affect plant growth?

Sunita placed 10 cress seeds on each of four Petri dishes. The dishes were given different amounts of water:

Dish A – no water
Dish B – 10 cm³ water,
Dish C – 20 cm³ water
Dish D – 30 cm³ water

All of the dishes were kept in an incubator at 25 °C for 5 days. At the end of this time the numbers of seeds which had germinated in each dish were counted.

a What question was being investigated in this experiment?

....

....

b Sunita made sure that the investigation was fair. How do you think she did this?

....

....

....

The results of the investigation are shown below:

Amount of water (cm³)	Number of seeds germinating
0	0
10	8
20	7
30	10

Sunita said that the results showed a pattern – as the amount of water increased, the number of seeds germinating also increased.

c Do the results in the table match Sunita's pattern?
Explain your answer.

....

....

....

....

Link – Exploring Science 7Db

Sc1 Skills for Key Stage 3 © Pearson Education Limited 2004

STARTER WORKSHEET

5 What affects the growth of sunflowers?

Anya wanted to investigate the growth of sunflowers.

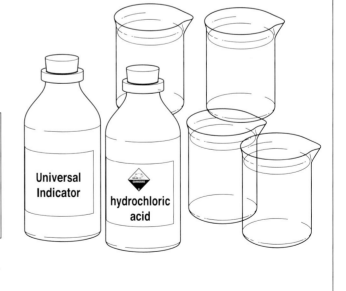

a What variables could she investigate?

....

....

....

b Choose a variable that Anya could change in her investigation and decide what she would need to measure.

....

....

c Complete Anya's question for investigation:

I want to find out how ....

affects ....

Link – Exploring Science 7Db

Sc1 Skills for Key Stage 3 © Pearson Education Limited 2004

✂

STARTER WORKSHEET

1 How do indigestion powders work?

Joel wanted to find out how four different indigestion powders affected the pH of hydrochloric (stomach) acid. He used the equipment shown on the right:

1 First he poured hydrochloric acid into four beakers.
2 Then he added different indigestion powders to each beaker.
3 He measured the pH of the acid using universal indicator paper.

Universal Indicator

hydrochloric acid

a What variables would Joel have to keep the same to make the investigation fair?

....

b What safety precautions should Joel take in this experiment?

....

....

Link – Exploring Science 7Ee

Sc1 Skills for Key Stage 3 © Pearson Education Limited 2004

STARTER WORKSHEET

2 How do indigestion powders work?

Joel wanted to find out how four different indigestion powders affected the pH of hydrochloric (stomach) acid.

Joel was given some hydrochloric acid that had the same pH as that found in the stomach.

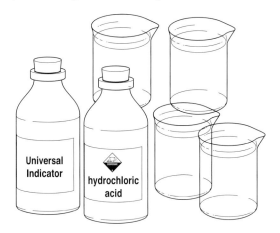

1 Joel put on his safety glasses.
2 He took four beakers and filled each with 20 cm³ of the hydrochloric acid.
3 He added 5 g of an indigestion powder to the first beaker, stirred it 10 times and then left it for 3 minutes.
4 He measured the pH of the acid using universal indicator paper and recorded the results.
5 He then repeated steps 3 and 4 for the other three indigestion powders.

a What piece of equipment would you recommend that Joel uses for:

  i measuring out the 20 cm³ of acid ....

  ii measuring out 5 g of the indigestion powders ....

  iii timing 3 minutes? ....

Joel obtained the following results:

FizzAcid powder – pH 8
pH 6 – ClearTums
pH 7 – AcidGone powder
indiclear – pH 6

b Design a table for these results. Remember to include all of the headings.

STARTER WORKSHEET

3 How do indigestion powders work?

Joel wanted to find out how four different indigestion powders affected the pH of some hydrochloric acid that had the same pH as that found in the stomach.

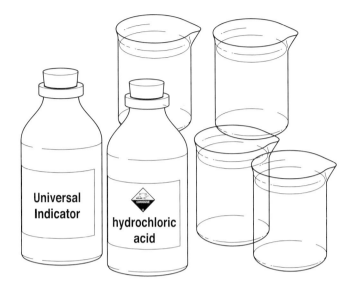

He carried out a fair test using different indigestion powders with 20 cm³ of the acid and obtained the following results:

Type of indigestion powder	pH of hydrochloric acid after 3 minutes
ClearTums	6
Indiclear	6
AcidGone	7
FizzAcid	8

Joel looked at the results and decided that AcidGone was the best indigestion powder to neutralise stomach acid.

a Is Joel's decision correct? Explain your answer. ....

....

b Which indigestion powder do you think is best? ....

c Explain your answer to part (b). ....

....

....

....

Joel's teacher said that the results of the investigation might not be accurate because the pH was read after 3 minutes.

d Explain why this might have affected the results.

....

....

Link – Exploring Science 7Ee

STARTER WORKSHEET

4 Does the pH of fizzy drinks affect the bubbles?

Jago decided to find out if the pH of fizzy drinks has any effect
on how long the drink makes bubbles after it is opened.

Here are the results of his investigations:

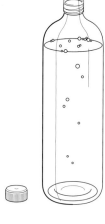

Type of fizzy drink	pH of drink	Time for bubbles to stop (seconds)
Fizzy Cola	7	320
Cherry Pop	5	175
Lemonade	6	280

a Which drink was the most acidic? ....

b How long did it take for Lemonade to stop making bubbles? ....

Jago predicted that the lower the pH (the more acidic a drink is), the longer the drink
stays fizzy.

c Was Jago's prediction right? ....

d Describe the pattern that you can see in the results.

....

....

Sc1 Skills for Key Stage 3 © Pearson Education Limited 200

STARTER WORKSHEET

5 Which is most acidic?

Amy wanted to find out which of three mystery
substances was the most acidic. She knew that
acids and sodium bicarbonate reacted together
by fizzing. Amy added three drops of each
substance to a dimple tile containing 2 cm³ of
sodium bicarbonate solution and watched what
happened.

Mystery substance	Observations
A	very little happened – there were one or two bubbles
B	there were lots of bubbles and fizzing
C	there were a few bubbles for about 5 seconds

Her results are shown on the right:

a What safety precaution would Amy have to take when using acids and alkalis?

....

b Suggest which piece of equipment would have been the most accurate to measure out

three drops of the mystery substances. ....

c Suggest which piece of equipment would have been the most accurate to measure out

2 cm³ of sodium bicarbonate. ....

d Which mystery substance do you think was the most acidic? ....

e Explain your answer. ....

....

Sc1 Skills for Key Stage 3 © Pearson Education Limited 2004

STARTER WORKSHEET

1 Investigating burning candles

Rima and Tasnim had four jam jars of different sizes. They wanted to find the volume of each jar.

a What piece of equipment would Rima and Tasnim need to measure the volume of the jars?

....

Rima lit a candle. She placed the first jam jar over the candle. Tasnim started timing as soon as the jar went over the candle. She stopped the timer when the candle went out. They then repeated the investigation with each jar.

b What was the question that Rima and Tasnim were investigating?

....

....

c Name:

   i the independent variable ....

   ii the dependent variable. ....

Sc1 Skills for Key Stage 3 © Pearson Education Limited 2004

STARTER WORKSHEET

2 Investigating burning candles

Rima and Tasnim were investigating how the volume of air in a jam jar affected the length of time it took for a burning candle to go out. Their results are shown on the right:

210 ml jar – 12 seconds

180 ml jar – 10 seconds

280 ml jar – 15 seconds

240 ml jar – 14 seconds

a Design a table for the results.

b Describe any pattern that you see in the results.

....

....

c Describe a scientific explanation for these results.

....

....

Sc1 Skills for Key Stage 3 © Pearson Education Limited 2004

STARTER WORKSHEET

3 Investigating burning candles

Rima and Tasnim were investigating how the volume of air in a jam jar affected the length of time it took for a burning candle to go out.

Their results are shown on the right:

Volume of jar (cm³)	Time for candle to go out (seconds)
180	10
210	12
240	14
280	15

a Which type of graph would be best for presenting these results? Explain your answer.

....

....

b Which variable would you place:

i on the *x*-axis ....

ii on the *y*-axis? ....

c Explain why the candle in the jar with the largest volume stayed alight longest.

....

....

Link – Exploring Science 7Fe

Sc1 Skills for Key Stage 3 © Pearson Education Limited 2004

STARTER WORKSHEET

4 What makes nails go rusty?

Matt and Ciaran took four test tubes each containing an iron nail and 20 cm³ of water. They then added common salt to the test tubes in the following amounts:

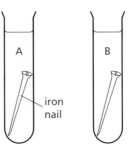

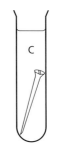

iron nail

They left the tubes in their classroom. After 7 days they looked to see how rusty the nails had become.

A – No salt   B – 2 g of salt   C – 4 g of salt   D – 6 g of salt

a What was the question that Matt and Ciaran were investigating?

....

b Why was test tube A left without any salt?

....

c Which variables did Matt and Ciaran keep the same to make the investigation fair?

....

....

Link – Exploring Science 7Fb

Sc1 Skills for Key Stage 3 © Pearson Education Limited 2004

STARTER WORKSHEET

5 Interpreting graphs

Look at the information in the graph.

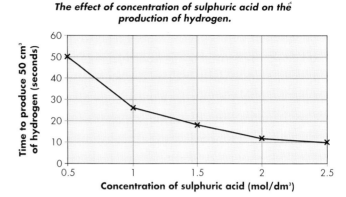

The effect of concentration of sulphuric acid on the production of hydrogen.

a Name:

  i the independent variable

  ....

  ....

  ii the dependent variable.

  ....

  ....

b Describe the pattern shown in the graph.

....

....

....

--✂

STARTER WORKSHEET

1 How does temperature affect the length of a steel rod?

Colin wanted to investigate how temperature would affect the length of a steel rod. He measured the length of the rod and then heated it by placing it in water that had been heated to a certain temperature. After 5 minutes he measured its length again. Colin then repeated the investigation at higher temperatures.

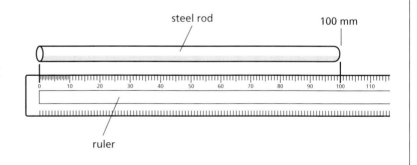

a In this investigation, name:

  i the independent variable ....

  ii the dependent variable. ....

b How could Colin have measured the temperature of the water accurately?

  ....

  ....

Link – Exploring Science 7Ge

STARTER WORKSHEET

2 How does temperature affect the length of a steel rod?

Colin wanted to investigate how temperature would affect the length of a steel rod. He measured the length of the rod and then heated it by placing it in water that had been heated to a certain temperature. After 5 minutes he measured its length again. Colin then repeated the investigation at higher temperatures.

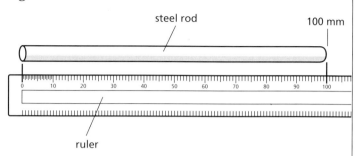

a What do you predict would happen to the length of the steel rod as its temperature increased?

....

b Explain your prediction using the particle model.

....

....

....

....

Link – Exploring Science 7Ge

✂ ....

STARTER WORKSHEET

3 How does mass affect melting ice?

Sandy and Megan decided to investigate how the mass of a piece of ice affected the speed at which it melted. Here is how they set up their investigation.

a What was the independent variable being investigated?

....

....

b What was the dependent variable being investigated?

....

....

c Was the investigation fair? Explain your answer.

....

....

....

STARTER WORKSHEET

4 How does mass affect melting ice?

Sandy and Megan decided to investigate how the mass of a piece of ice affected the speed at which it melted. Here is how they set up their investigation.

Megan's friend told them that their idea was unfair because the pieces of ice were different shapes and because the different parts of the room they had selected had different temperatures.

a Explain how this investigation could be carried out again, overcoming these difficulties.

....

....

....

....

b What equipment would you need to accurately measure the mass of the ice?

....

Sc1 Skills for Key Stage 3 © Pearson Education Limited 2004

✂

STARTER WORKSHEET

5 Is the diffusion of tea through water affected by temperature?

An investigation into the diffusion of tea through water at different temperatures was carried out by measuring the distance moved by the brown colour from a tea bag in a beaker of water. Use the results in this table to answer the questions that follow.

Temperature of water (°C)	Distance tea diffused through the water in 2 minutes (mm)
20	2
40	16
60	35
80	66

a Name the independent variable. ....

b State the question that is being investigated. ....

....

c Describe the pattern shown in the results, using your knowledge of particle theory.

....

....

....

Link – Exploring Science 7Gd

Sc1 Skills for Key Stage 3 © Pearson Education Limited 2004

25

STARTER WORKSHEET

1 Interpreting graphs

a What question is being investigated in the graph below? ....

....

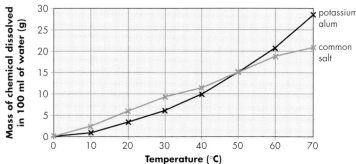

The effect of temperature on the solubility of common salt and potassium alum in water.

....

....

....

....

....

....

b At what temperature are salt and potassium alum equally soluble? ....

c Which chemical shown on the graph is most soluble at 40 °C?

....

Link – Exploring Science 7He

Sc1 Skills for Key Stage 3 © Pearson Education Limited 2004

STARTER WORKSHEET

2 Investigating solubility

Look at the table of information on the solubility of different substances.

Substance	Solubility (g/100 cm³ of water at 20 °C)
common salt	37.9
bicarbonate of soda	8.6
sugar	203.9

a Which substance is the most soluble at 20 °C? ....

b What mass of bicarbonate of soda would dissolve in 200 cm³ of water at 20 °C? ....

c Explain how you worked out your answer to (b). ....

....

203.9 g of sugar will dissolve in 100 cm³ of water at 20 °C.

d What mass of sugar do you predict would dissolve in 100 cm³ of water at 40 °C?

☐ Less than 203.9 g   ☐ Exactly 203.9 g   ☐ More than 203.9 g

e Explain your answer to (d).

....

....

Link – Exploring Science 7He

Sc1 Skills for Key Stage 3 © Pearson Education Limited 2004

STARTER WORKSHEET

3 **Solutions and mass**

Barry took some water in a beaker and measured its
mass as 100.5 g. He then added 2 g of common salt.
The salt dissolved immediately.

a What will the new mass of the beaker and its
contents be?

....

b Explain your answer to part (a).

....

....

Barry then left the beaker and its contents in a warm room
over the lunch hour. When he returned to the classroom he measured its mass again.

c What do you think will have happened to the mass of the beaker and its contents over
the lunch hour?

☐ It will have decreased.   ☐ It will have stayed the same.   ☐ It will have increased.

d Explain your answer to part (c).

....

Sc1 Skills for Key Stage 3 © Pearson Education Limited 2004

STARTER WORKSHEET

4 **Does adding salt affect the boiling point of water?**

Raul and Luis want to investigate how the amount of salt
dissolved in 100 cm³ of water affects its boiling point.

Plan how you would do this. Include details on:

a the equipment you would use

b the range of masses of salt that you would add to
the water

c any safety precautions you would include.

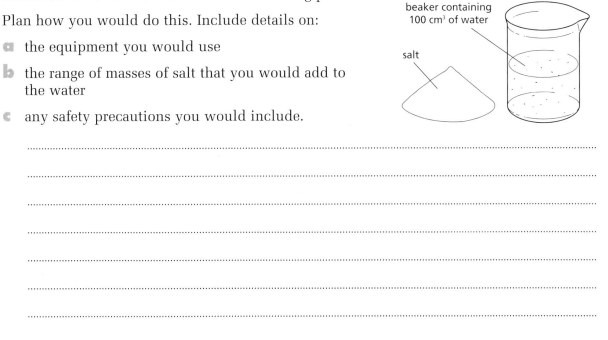

beaker containing
100 cm³ of water

salt

....

....

....

....

....

....

....

....

Sc1 Skills for Key Stage 3 © Pearson Education Limited 2004

27

STARTER WORKSHEET

5 Interpreting graphs

The graph shows the results of an experiment carried out in a classroom at 20 °C. Look carefully at the graph.

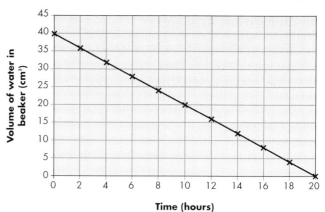

a What question is being investigated in the graph?

....

....

b What pattern can you see in the results?

....

In this investigation all of the water in the beaker had gone after 20 hours.

c How long would it have taken for all of the water to have gone if the temperature of the room had been 30 °C?

☐ less than 20 hours   ☐ 20 hours   ☐ more than 20 hours

d Explain your answer to part (c).

....

....

Sc1 Skills for Key Stage 3 © Pearson Education Limited 2004

STARTER WORKSHEET

1 Comparing fuels

Mustapha wanted to find out which fuel gave out most heat energy. He set some fuels alight in a metal dish and measured how much the temperature of water in a test tube held over them increased.

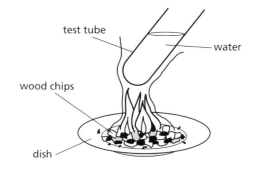

a What variables would Mustapha need to keep the same in order to make the investigation fair?

....

....

b What equipment would you recommend Mustapha chooses to measure:

i the mass of fuel used ....

ii the temperature of the water? ....

c Suggest one safety precaution that Mustapha should take.

....

Link – Exploring Science 7Ia

Sc1 Skills for Key Stage 3 © Pearson Education Limited 2004

STARTER WORKSHEET

2 Investigating fuels

Many fuels leave waste materials behind when they are burnt. Zina wanted to investigate this. She decided to investigate three fuels to find out which was best. Here is her plan for the investigation:

1 dish — wood chips
electronic balance

> 1   Weigh out some fuel.
> 2   Put the fuel in a metal dish and set it alight using a match.
> 3   Weigh the ashes left at the end when the fire has gone out.

Consider Zina's plan.

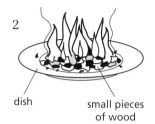

2
dish — small pieces of wood

a Is it clear what question is being investigated? Explain why.

....

....

....

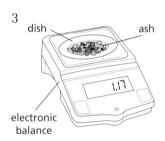

3
dish — ash
electronic balance

b What other details should Zina add to her plan?

....

....

....

Sc1 Skills for Key Stage 3 © Pearson Education Limited 2004

STARTER WORKSHEET

3 Investigating fuels

Look at the chart on the right and the data table below.

Fuel usage in the UK.

Fuel	Percentage usage
coal	20
gas	
oil	50

a Which segment of the pie chart represents which fuel?

A = ...

B = ...

C = ...

b Work out the percentage of gas usage in the UK.

....

....

STARTER WORKSHEET

4 Interpreting data

The table shows data gathered from a solar cell linked to an ammeter.

Light intensity (lux)	Current (amps)
0	0.0
10	0.2
20	0.4
30	0.6
40	
50	1.0

From the table:

a name the independent variable ....

b name the dependent variable ....

c predict the missing value of current (amps) at 40 lux. Explain your answer.

....

....

....

Link – Exploring Science 7Ic

Sc1 Skills for Key Stage 3 © Pearson Education Limited 200

✂ ....

STARTER WORKSHEET

5 Solar cells

Look carefully at the graph showing how the amount of light shining on a solar cell affects the current which it makes.

a Describe the pattern that you can see in these results.

....

....

....

b Use your scientific knowledge to explain why this pattern has been found.

....

....

....

Link – Exploring Science 7Ic

Sc1 Skills for Key Stage 3 © Pearson Education Limited 2004

STARTER WORKSHEET

1 Does length of wire affect the current it carries?

Ravinder and Susan were investigating how the length of a piece of wire affected the current flowing through it. Here is a graph of their results.

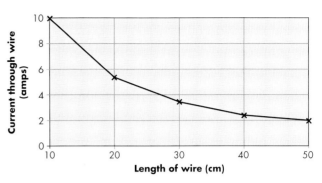

a Name a piece of equipment that Ravinder and Susan might have used to measure the electrical current.

....

b An independent variable is being changed. Which one?

....

c What dependent variable is being measured?

....

d Describe how the length of a piece of wire affects the current flowing through it.

....

....

Link – Exploring Science 7Jb

STARTER WORKSHEET

2 Does the number of bulbs in a series circuit affect their brightness?

Karen decided to investigate how the number of bulbs in a series circuit affected their brightness. When one bulb was connected to a 4.5 V battery it shone brightly.

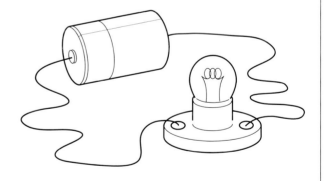

a Complete the sentence below to make a prediction about the effect of increasing the number of bulbs in the series circuit:

I think that as the number of bulbs increases, the ....

....

b Use your scientific knowledge to explain why you made this prediction.

....

....

Link – Exploring Science 7Jc

STARTER WORKSHEET

3 Investigating voltage and current

Here are the results of an investigation into how the voltage of a power pack affected the current flowing through a circuit.

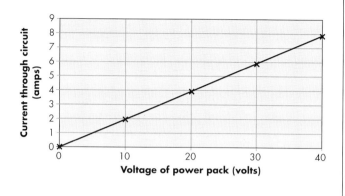

a Describe the pattern that you can see in the graph linking the voltage of the power pack and the current flowing through the circuit.

....

....

....

b Explain why this pattern is present.

....

....

....

Link – Exploring Science 7Jc

STARTER WORKSHEET

4 Is the amount of electrical current in a wire linked to the heat given out?

Danielle wanted to find out how the amount of electrical current flowing through a wire affected how much heat the wire gave out.

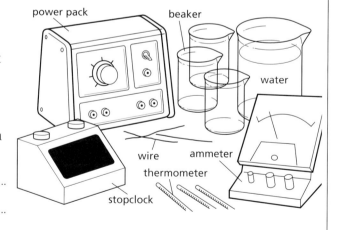

a Describe how Danielle could investigate this question using the equipment shown here:

....

....

....

....

....

b List the variables that would have to be controlled in this investigation.

....

....

Link – Exploring Science 7Jd

STARTER WORKSHEET

5 Interpreting data

Look at the data in the table:

Material (20 cm lengths)	Amount of current flowing when connected to a 9 V battery (amps)
copper	12.4
nichrome	2.7
manganin	4.5
plastic	0

a Name:

  i the independent variable ....

  ii the dependent variable. ....

b Using the information in the table and your scientific knowledge, explain why electrical cables are made with:

  i copper wire

    ....

  ii a plastic coating.

    ....

Link – Exploring Science 7Ja

Sc1 Skills for Key Stage 3 © Pearson Education Limited 2004

STARTER WORKSHEET

1 Investigating springs

The table shows some of the results of an investigation on springs.

Force	Extension of spring (mm)
0	0
1	40
2	80
3	
4	160

a What question is being investigated?

  ....

b What is missing from the table headings?

  ....

c Predict the size of the missing extension when the force is 3.

  ....

d Explain how you made this prediction.

  ....

Link – Exploring Science 7Kc

Sc1 Skills for Key Stage 3 © Pearson Education Limited 2004

STARTER WORKSHEET

2 Investigating grip in shoes

Ruth wanted to investigate which of three different shoes had the most grip. Ruth put bags of sand in each shoe to hold them down. She then pulled them over a surface with a forcemeter.

a What variables would Ruth have to keep the same to make the investigation fair?

....

....

b Using clues from the diagrams of the shoes, predict which shoe you think will have the

greatest grip. ....

c Explain why you have chosen this shoe.

....

....

Link – Exploring Science 7Kd

Sc1 Skills for Key Stage 3 © Pearson Education Limited 2004

STARTER WORKSHEET

3 Is weight affected by water?

Bill wanted to investigate the effect of submersion in water on the weight of a toy car.

Use the diagram to answer the following questions:

a What is the reading of force on the forcemeter? (Remember to include the units.)

....

b What do you predict will happen to the reading when the toy car is lowered into the water?

....

....

c Explain your prediction.

....

....

....

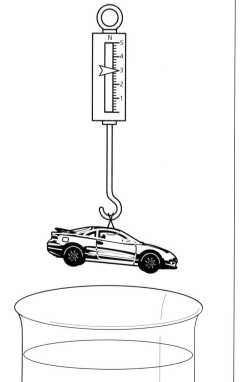

Link – Exploring Science 7Kb

Sc1 Skills for Key Stage 3 © Pearson Education Limited 2004

STARTER WORKSHEET

4 Interpreting graphs

The graph on the right describes the movement of a cat in a garden.

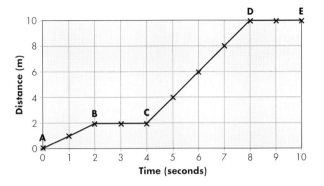

a Describe the movement of the cat in each of the sections of the graph, A to E.

....

....

....

....

....

b What is the difference in the movement of the cat in section A – B compared with C – D?

....

....

Link – Exploring Science 7Ke

STARTER WORKSHEET

5 Investigating stopping distances

The table shows the distance needed to stop cars with different amounts of tread (the grooves on a tyre's surface) on their tyres in varying road conditions.

Condition of tyre tread	Number of metres needed to stop a car travelling at 50 km/h		
	Dry road	Slightly wet road	Very wet road
new	20	30	45
slightly worn	30	45	70
very worn	45	70	120

a How does the wetness of a road affect the distance needed to stop a car?

....

b The law says that car tyres must have a minimum amount of tread to be legal. Explain why there is a minimum tread level.

....

....

Link – Exploring Science 7Kd

STARTER WORKSHEET

1 The planets and their orbits

Look at the table of information about the first four planets of the Solar System.

Planet	Distance from the Sun (million km)	Time to orbit the Sun (Earth years)
Mercury	58	0.2
Venus	108	0.6
Earth	150	1.0
Mars	228	1.9

a What pattern can you see linking the distance from the Sun and the time taken to orbit the Sun?

....

....

b Explain any reasons for this pattern.

....

....

Sc1 Skills for Key Stage 3 © Pearson Education Limited 2004

✂ ···

STARTER WORKSHEET

2 Investigating shadows

The picture shows the position of a shadow from a stick at 6 am.

a Predict which position you think the shadow would be in at 6 pm the same day. Choose the correct letter from the diagram.

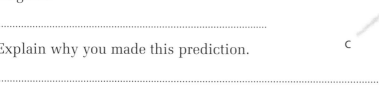

....

b Explain why you made this prediction.

....

....

....

....

....

....

Link – Exploring Science 7La

Sc1 Skills for Key Stage 3 © Pearson Education Limited 2004

STARTER WORKSHEET

3 Investigating shadows

The picture on the right shows the length of a shadow at 1 pm on a sunny summer's day in the UK.

a How would the shadow look different at 1 pm on a sunny winter's day in the UK?

....

....

....

....

b Explain your answer to part (a).

....

....

....

Link – Exploring Science 7Lc

Sc1 Skills for Key Stage 3 © Pearson Education Limited 2004

✂

STARTER WORKSHEET

4 The planets and their gravity

Look at the information in the table:

Planet	Mass of planet compared to Earth (Earth = 1)	Force of gravity (N/kg)
Venus	0.8	9
Earth	1.0	10
Mars	0.1	
Jupiter	320.0	26
Saturn	95.0	11

a Describe the pattern that you can see between the mass of a planet and its gravity.

....

....

b Using the information in the table, predict the force of gravity found on the surface of Mars. Explain your answer.

....

....

....

Sc1 Skills for Key Stage 3 © Pearson Education Limited 2004

STARTER WORKSHEET

5 Interpreting graphs

The graphs show the variation in light intensity, temperature and shadow length during a summer's day:

For each of the graphs, A, B and C, decide which variable it represents and write your reasons for this choice.

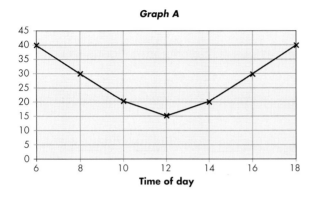

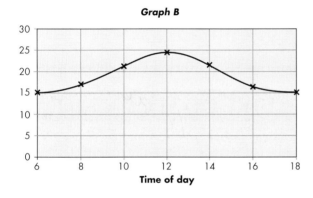

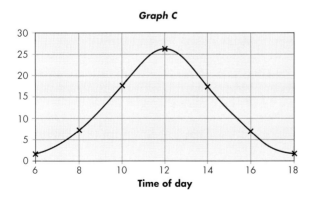

Sc1 Skills for Key Stage 3 © Pearson Education Limited 2004

STARTER THINKING SKILLS

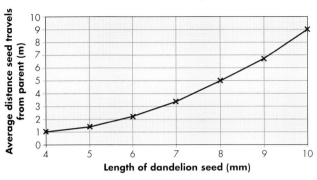

The effect of the length of a dandelion seed on the average distance it is transported from the parent plant.

Look at the graph above. What does it tell us?

....

Graphs help us to answer questions and see patterns in results. What questions could you ask about this graph that other people in your class could answer?

....

....

Sc1 Skills for Key Stage 3 © Pearson Education Limited 2004

STARTER THINKING SKILLS

Look at the graph. What does it tell us?

....

....

....

....

....

....

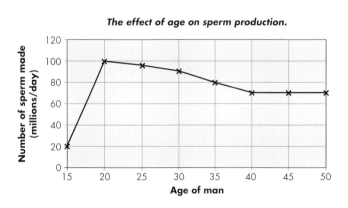

The effect of age on sperm production.

Graphs help us to answer questions and see patterns in results. What questions could you ask about this graph that other people in your class could answer?

....

....

....

....

Sc1 Skills for Key Stage 3 © Pearson Education Limited 2004

STARTER THINKING SKILLS

Look at the graph. What does it tell us?

....

....

....

....

....

....

Average daytime temperature throughout the year.

Graphs help us to answer questions and see patterns in results. What questions could you ask about this graph that other people in your class could answer?

....

....

....

....

Sc1 Skills for Key Stage 3 © Pearson Education Limited 2004

STARTER THINKING SKILLS

Look at the graph. What does it tell us?

....

....

....

....

....

....

The effect of the amount of fertiliser on the number of apples produced per tree.

Graphs help us to answer questions and see patterns in results. What questions could you ask about this graph that other people in your class could answer?

....

....

....

....

Sc1 Skills for Key Stage 3 © Pearson Education Limited 2004

STARTER **THINKING SKILLS**

Look at the graph. What does it tell us?

....

....

....

....

....

....

The effect of time after opening on the pH of wine.

Graphs help us to answer questions and see patterns in results. What questions could you ask about this graph that other people in your class could answer?

....

....

....

....

Sc1 Skills for Key Stage 3 © Pearson Education Limited 2004

✂

STARTER **THINKING SKILLS**

Concentration of sulphuric acid (mol/dm³)	Volume of hydrogen released when sulphuric acid is added to 1 g of magnesium filings in 1 minute
0.5	2.0
1.0	4.0
2.0	6.0
1.5	5.5
2.5	6.5

Look at the table. What does it tell us?

....

Tables present data and help us to answer questions and see patterns in results. What questions could you ask about this table that other people in your class could answer?

....

....

....

Sc1 Skills for Key Stage 3 © Pearson Education Limited 2004

STARTER THINKING SKILLS

Volume of air in tyre (cm³)	Pressure of air in tyres (N/cm²)
100	8
200	16
300	24
400	
500	40

Look at the table. What does it tell us?

....

Tables present data and help us to answer questions and see patterns in results. What questions could you ask about this table that other people in your class could answer?

....

....

....

✂ ●

STARTER THINKING SKILLS

Look at the graph. What does it tell us?

....

....

....

....

....

....

The effect of the volume of water on the amount of salt that it can dissolve.

Graphs help us to answer questions and see patterns in results. What questions could you ask about this graph that other people in your class could answer?

....

....

....

....

STARTER **THINKING SKILLS**

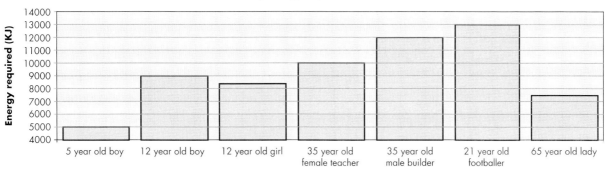

Daily energy requirements.

Look at the graph above. What does it tell us?

....

Graphs help us to answer questions and see patterns in results. What questions could you ask about this graph that other people in your class could answer?

....

....

Sc1 Skills for Key Stage 3 © Pearson Education Limited 2004

✂

STARTER **THINKING SKILLS**

Number of bulbs in the circuit	Current (amps)
1	0.3
2	0.21
3	0.17
4	0.15

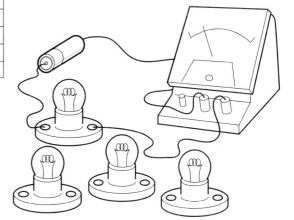

Look at the table. What does it tell us?

....

....

....

....

Tables present data and help us to answer questions and see patterns in results. What questions could you ask about this table that other people in your class could answer?

....

....

....

Sc1 Skills for Key Stage 3 © Pearson Education Limited 2004

43

STARTER **THINKING SKILLS**

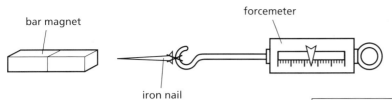

bar magnet

forcemeter

iron nail

Look at the table. What does it tell us?

....

....

....

Distance of magnet (cm)	Force on iron nail (N)
2	2.0
4	1.0
6	0.6
8	0.4
10	0.3

Tables present data and help us to answer questions and see patterns in results. What questions could you ask about this table that other people in your class could answer?

....

....

....

Sc1 Skills for Key Stage 3 © Pearson Education Limited 2004

 ●●●

UNIT 7L **THE SOLAR SYSTEM AND BEYOND**

STARTER **THINKING SKILLS**

Distance from Sun (million km)	Speed of comet (km/seconds)
500	4
400	8
300	14
200	22
100	32

Look at the table. What does it tell us?

....

Tables present data and help us to answer questions and see patterns in results. What questions could you ask about this table that other people in your class could answer?

....

....

....

Sc1 Skills for Key Stage 3 © Pearson Education Limited 2004

Unit 7A **CELLS**

The activities in this unit concern looking at cells and an investigation into the growth of pollen tubes. The activities can be used to help pupils identify variables, plan use of appropriate equipment, develop fair procedures and become familiar with interpretation of tables and graphs.

1 **a** The microscope would give the greatest magnification to clearly see the plant cells.

   b ×4

   c When first using a microscope the lowest magnification should be selected, brought into focus and then progressively higher magnifications chosen until the desired image is produced.

   d The mirror was not positioned correctly so insufficient light was being reflected from the light source into the microscope.

2 **a** **i** Concentration of sugar solution. **ii** Length of pollen tube.

   b The 20% figure is missing which will affect the subsequent drawing of a graph.

3 **a** To allow them to identify any unusual/anomalous results (allow the answers, to compare the results with each other/to check the reliability of the results).

   b Volume of sugar solution, time left in solution, type of pollen grain.

   c To make it a fair test and show which variable was having the effect.

   d mm

4 **a** 30%

   b There are two possible answers that can be discussed here:

   Repeat the investigation a minimum of five times to see whether the same pattern is found.

   Investigate the growth of pollen grains within a finer range of sugar solution concentrations, e.g. 25, 27, 29, 31, 33 and 35% to find out whether the optimal concentration really is 30%.

   c Present the results as a line graph.

   d Any number below 7.

5 **a** **i** Concentration of sugar. **ii** Average length of pollen tube.

   b **i** 2 mm – found by drawing a line up from 5% until the line of the graph is reached and then across to the *y*-axis. **ii** 25% – found by drawing a line across from 10 mm until the line of the graph is reached and then down to the *x*-axis.

   c A microscope.

   d Graph to show how the concentration of sugar affects the average length of pollen tubes.

Extension – Investigate how the strength of sugar solution affects the growth of pollen tubes.

   Link – Exploring Science 7Ae.

Unit 7B **REPRODUCTION**

The activities in this unit concern the development of the fetus in the uterus leading to questions relating to variation. The activities can be used to help pupils identify variables, form predictions, produce tables and graphs and identify and describe patterns.

1 **a** **i** Sperm cell tail length. **ii** Speed of sperm cell.

   b As the tail length increases, the speed increases (or the inverse – as the tail length decreases, the speed decreases). *Or* The longer the tail, the higher the speed (or the inverse – the shorter the tail, the lower the speed).

   Note to teachers: A μm (also known as a micron) is one thousandth of a millimetre or 10^{-6} m. This unit could be used as an opportunity to discuss concepts of size and scale.

2 **a** As the number of cigarettes smoked increased, the birth weight of the baby decreased (or the inverse – as the number of cigarettes smoked decreased, the birth weight of the baby increased). *Or* The more cigarettes were smoked, the lower the baby's birth weight (or the inverse – the fewer cigarettes were smoked, the higher the baby's birth weight).

   b General health of the mother, diet of mother, level of blood supply to fetus, health of fetus, length of time fetus spent in the womb.

3 a i 300 mm – found by drawing a line up from 20 weeks until the line of the graph is reached and then across to the *y*-axis. **ii** 25 weeks – found by drawing a line across from 400 mm until the line of the graph is reached and then down to the *x*-axis. **iii** Between 15 and 20 weeks.

b This is the point where the graph is the steepest (greatest gradient).

4 a Units are missing from the foot length column – cm.

b As the width of the foot increased, the length of the foot increased (or the inverse – as the width of the foot decreased, the length of the foot decreased). *Or* The wider the foot, the longer the foot (or the inverse – the narrower the foot, the shorter the foot).

c 17–20 cm – estimated by looking at the pattern of quantities shown in the table of results.

5 a 155 cm

b Between the ages of 10–12.

c A line graph or a bar graph – try to encourage pupils to suggest a type of graph rather than just answering 'a graph'. Ideally this graph would be a line graph as these data are a continuous series with intermediate points which could be interpolated.

Extension – Conduct a survey of the members of the class to practise the skills of designing tables and producing graphs.

Unit 7C ENVIRONMENT AND FEEDING RELATIONSHIPS

The activities in this unit concern measurements of environmental factors and how changes in conditions affect living creatures. The activities can be used to help pupils to form questions to investigate, make predictions, plan fair tests and interpret data in tables.

1 a Temperature will decrease because the Sun will have set and heating systems in the school will be switched off when the school is shut.

b Light intensity will decrease because the Sun will have set and classroom lights turned off when the school is shut.

c Noise levels will decrease when the pupils and staff go home and then decrease further as traffic noise reduces as midnight approaches.

2 a Datalogger with temperature probe.

b As a line graph.

c/d Either answer with an explanation is acceptable:
No, because the outside temperature may be different and affect the temperature of the classroom.
Yes, because all of the conditions would be the same in the classroom.

3 a Possible variables could be: temperature, humidity, light intensity.

b Pupils should devise a plan in which woodlice are placed in varying environments and their behaviour observed. This could be in the form of simple observations in a natural habitat or, alternatively, using some form of choice chamber where appropriate conditions have been manufactured.

4 a What affect does the *amount of cotton wool* have on the *temperature of the water?*

b Amount/volume of water in the can, initial temperature of the water, material the cans were made from, size of the cans.

c The can with three layers of cotton wool.

d Because this can had the most insulation to prevent loss of heat.

5 a This was the control of the investigation. It allowed Arwen and Howard to compare whether it was the cotton wool that was making a difference to the results.

b The three-layered can.

c Using a datalogger and temperature probe.

d Make a lid for the cans so no heat can escape by convection. *Or* Lift the cans off the surface so heat cannot be transferred by conduction.

Extension – Plan and carry out an investigation into the way in which the environmental factors of the classroom alter over a 24 hour period. Use dataloggers to collect information and ICT to present data in the form of graphs.

Link – Exploring Science 7Ca

Unit 7D **VARIATION AND CLASSIFICATION**

The activities in this unit concern the effect of the environment on the growth of plants and an investigation into the growth of sunflowers. The activities can be used to help pupils form questions, plan fair investigations and interpret data in tables to identify patterns in data and draw conclusions.

1 a

Length of leaf (cm)	Number of prickles
3.0	5
3.5	7
4.0	9
4.5	11
5.0	13

Award points for the following features: independent variable (length of leaf) in first column; unit included; data presented in order of increasing magnitude.

b As the length of leaf increased, the number of prickles increased (or the inverse – as the length of leaf decreased, the number of prickles decreased). *Or* The longer the leaf the more prickles (or the inverse – the shorter the leaf the less prickles).

c Five leaves is not a big enough sample size to be sure of a pattern. Gerda would need to measure several more leaves to be sure of its validity.

2 a Amount of fertiliser used, amount of water added, time left to grow; way in which fertiliser was added, way in which the length of the grass was measured, etc.

b As a control to compare with the areas where fertilisers were used.

c Use an electric balance.

3 a Sunflowers may have started off at different heights, the amounts of water and temperatures varied when they should have been kept constant.

b Amil should have: measured the plants at the start and end of the investigation so that growth could be measured; given all plants equal amounts of water; kept all plants at the same temperature.

c To try to reach sunlight so they can make food.

4 a How does the amount of water affect the number of seeds germinating?

b Same type of dish, same number of seeds, kept at the same temperature, same amount of time left.

c They do not match the relationship 'as the amount of water increased, the number of seeds germinating increased'. Pupils should be able to explain that the 10 cm^3 result is too high (or the 20 cm^3 too low) to support the suggested pattern.

5 a Examples of independent variables might include: light intensity, amount of water, temperature, colour of light, amount of earth sunflower grown in, type of soil sunflower grown in.

b Good examples of dependent variables to be measured might include: The mass of the plant, height, number of leaves.

c I want to find out how *the amount of water* affects *the height of a sunflower*. Accept similar answers.

Extension – Plan and carry out an investigation into the germination of cress seedlings.

Unit 7E **ACIDS AND ALKALIS**

The activities in this unit concern an investigation into the neutralisation of stomach acid using indigestion powders and further investigations into pH. The activities can be used to help pupils plan fair tests in which due regard is given to safety and the suitable selection of equipment, the interpretation of results and description of patterns in data.

1 a Same volume of hydrochloric acid, same mass of indigestion powder, same amount of time to react, same level of stirring.

b Safety glasses should always be worn; wipe up any spills.

2 a **i** 50 cm³ measuring cylinder or syringe – extend pupils by asking how the measuring cylinder should be used. **ii** Accurate electronic balance. **iii** Stopwatch or other timing device.

b

Type of indigestion powder	pH of hydrochloric acid after 3 minutes
ClearTums	6
Indiclear	6
AcidGone	7
FizzAcid	8

In this table the order of indigestion powders is unimportant as it is a discrete variable.

3 a and **b** Discuss pupils' answers with the emphasis on what is meant by the term 'best'.

c The most powerful neutraliser amongst the powders is FizzAcid as it has left an alkaline pH after 3 minutes reaction time. However, it may be that another of the indigestion powders is the quickest acting whilst another neutralises without forming any excess gas. This can be used by teachers as a point to discuss the problem of asking which indigestion powder is 'best'.

d The powders may not have had time to react fully.

4 a Cherry Pop

b 280 seconds

c no

d As the pH of the drink increased, the time for the bubbles to stop increased (or the inverse – as the pH of the drink decreased, the time for the bubbles to stop decreased). *Or* The higher the pH, the longer the time for bubbles to stop (or the inverse – the lower the pH, the shorter the time for bubbles to stop).

5 a Wearing eye protection; wiping up spills.

b A pipette or dropper.

c A 5 cm³ or 10 cm³ measuring cylinder placed on a level surface.

d solution B

e Solution B was the most acidic because it caused the largest reaction with the sodium bicarbonate.

Extension – Plan and carry out an investigation to determine the most effective indigestion remedy and write a newspaper report to present the findings.

Link – Exploring Science 7Ee

Unit 7F SIMPLE CHEMICAL REACTIONS

The activities in this unit concern investigations into burning, corrosion and the reactions of metals and acids. The activities can be used to help pupils identify variables, present results in tables and graphs and to describe patterns in data.

1 a A measuring cylinder of appropriate size.

b Does the volume of air in a jam jar affect how long it takes for a burning candle to go out?

c **i** The volume of air in the jam jar. **ii** The time taken for the candle to go out.

2 a

Volume of jar (cm³)	Time for candle to go out (seconds)
180	10
210	12
240	14
280	15
400	25

b As the volume of the jar increased, the time taken for the candle to go out increased (or the inverse – as the volume of the jar decreased, the time taken for the candle to go out decreased). *Or* The larger the volume of the jar, the longer the candle stayed alight (or the inverse – the smaller the volume of the jar, the less time the candle stayed alight).

c The candle uses oxygen to burn. A bigger jar will have a greater volume of air in it, therefore more oxygen, so the candle will burn for longer.

3 a A line graph is best suited for this situation as it involves two sets of numerical data, both of which are continuous variables. Bar graphs are used where the independent variable is discrete and the dependent variable continuous.

  b i Volume of the jar (independent variable). ii Time for candle to go out (dependent variable).

  c The jar with the largest volume contained the most oxygen, the gas needed for candles to burn.

4 a How does the amount of salt affect the rusting of the iron nail?

  b As a control to compare with the test tubes containing salt.

  c Same volume of water, same type of nail, same time left in test tubes.

5 a i The concentration of sulphuric acid. ii The time to produce 50 cm³ of hydrogen.

  b As the concentration of the acid increases the time taken to produce 50 cm³ of hydrogen decreases (or the inverse – as the concentration of the acid decreases the time taken to produce 50 cm³ of hydrogen increases). *Or* The higher the concentration of acid, the shorter the time taken to produce 50 cm³ of hydrogen (or the inverse – the lower the concentration of acid, the longer the time taken to produce 50 cm³ of hydrogen).

Extension – Investigate whether all metals react in the same way when placed in contact with acids.

  Link – Exploring Science 7Fb

Unit 7G PARTICLE MODEL OF SOLIDS, LIQUIDS AND GASES

The activities in this unit concern the use of the particle theory to explain and predict expansion, melting and diffusion. The activities can be used to help pupils identify factors, make predictions using a scientific model, describe patterns in results and evaluate experimental methods.

1 a i The temperature of the rod. ii The length of the rod after heating.

  b Using a temperature probe and datalogger or a digital thermometer.

2 a A correct prediction would be 'As the temperature of the rod increased its length increased'. However, credit should be given to any well formed prediction regardless of its veracity.

  b Pupils should use the particle theory to explain their prediction, e.g. because the particle theory says that as solids heat up, the particles become more and more energetic and take up more space. This increases the overall length of the rod.

  It should be noted that answers suggesting increases in the spaces *between* particles are not valid when referring to solids or liquids, only gases.

3 a The mass of the piece of ice.

  b The time taken for the ice to melt.

  c The investigation was not fair. The reasons for this should include: variation in the shape of the ice; differing temperature of locations in the classroom.

4 a Pupils should ensure that all pieces of ice are of similar shape, e.g. all cubes, and that they are kept in the same temperature conditions.

  b An electronic balance.

5 a Temperature of water.

  b How does the temperature of water affect the distance that tea diffuses through water in 2 minutes (or, the speed of diffusion of tea in water).

  c As the temperature of the water increases, the distance the tea diffuses increases (or the inverse – as the temperature of the water decreases, the distance the tea diffused decreases). *Or* The higher the temperature of the water, the greater the distance the tea diffuses (or the inverse – the lower the temperature of the water, the shorter the distance the tea diffuses). This happens because as the temperature of the water increases, the temperature of the particles of tea also increases, giving the particles more energy and causing them to move faster.

Extension – Plan and carry out an investigation into the effect of temperature on diffusion.

  Link – Exploring Science 7Gd

Unit 7H **SOLUTIONS**

The activities in this unit mainly concern issues about dissolving. The activities can be used to help pupils make predictions, plan experimental procedures and interpret tables and graphs.

1 a   How does temperature affect the solubility of salt and potassium alum?

    b   50 °C – where the lines intersect.

    c   common salt

2 a   sugar

    b   17.2 g

    c $8.6 \times 2 = 17.2$ g of bicarbonate of soda

    d   More than 203.9 g.

    e   As the temperature of a solvent increases, the solubility of the solute increases. Pupils may explain this in terms of the particle theory and an increase in the energy of the solvent molecules breaking more bonds of the solute.

3 a $100.5 + 2 = 102.5$ g

    b   Although the salt cannot be seen it is still present in the beaker so the total mass of the beaker and contents will increase by the full amount of the mass of the salt.

    c   It will have decreased.

    d   Some of the mass of water in the beaker would have evaporated, so reducing the overall mass.

4 a   Bunsen burner, equipment to measure temperature (e.g. thermometer or datalogger with temperature probe), electronic balance, measuring cylinder.

    b   Any suitable range can be accepted although these should be evenly spread, e.g. 0 g, 1 g, 2 g, 3 g, 4 g.

    c   Wearing of safety glasses, correct use of thermometer, wiping up of any spills.

5 a   Accept any answers that link the amount of water in the beaker to time, e.g. *How does the volume of water in a beaker change over time?* or, *How does time affect the amount of water in a beaker?*

    b   As the time increases, the volume of water in the beaker decreases (or the inverse – as the time decreases the volume of water in the beaker increases). *Or* The longer the time, the lower the volume of water in the beaker (or the inverse – the shorter the time, the higher the volume of water in the beaker).

    c   Less than 20 hours (as the rate of evaporation would have been greater at 30 °C).

    d   As the temperature of the surroundings increases, the rate of evaporation of water increases, so more water would evaporate from the beaker in a shorter period of time.

Extension – Plan and carry out an investigation into the effect of temperature of solvent on the solubility of a solute (e.g. salt or sugar). This data can then be presented in tables and graphs allowing further predictions / interpolations to be made.

Unit 7I **ENERGY RESOURCES**

The activities in this unit concern the release of energy from fuels and an investigation into the use of a solar cell. The activities can be used to help pupils identify variables, plan and evaluate fair investigations with appropriate selection of equipment and identify and describe patterns in results.

1 a   The mass of the fuel, the volume of water in the test tube, the starting temperature of the water, the distance the test tube is held from the fuel, the way in which the fuel was lit.

    b   **i** Electronic balance. **ii** Thermometer or datalogger with temperature probe.

    c   Safety glasses/tying back long hair/ensuring that the bench surface is well protected.

2 a   No, discuss the idea of 'best' and reinforce the need to be specific about what is actually being investigated. Ask pupils to come up with a suggestion for what the question could be, e.g. 'Which fuel leaves behind the least ash?'

    b   Missing elements include: variables – names of fuel used; equipment – used to measure original mass of fuels and of the waste products; quantities – of fuels used and details of how the investigation would be kept fair; safety: no precautions mentioned.

3 a A = oil, B = coal, C = gas.

b 100 − 70 = 30% gas usage.

4 a light intensity

b current

c 0.8 amps – discuss with pupils how this figure was reached by an examination of the pattern in results available.

5 a As the light intensity increases, the current increases (or the inverse – as the light intensity decreases, the current decreases). *Or* The higher the light intensity, the higher the current (or the inverse – the lower the light intensity, the lower the current).

b As the light intensity increases the amount of light energy available to be converted into electrical energy increases as well.

Extension – Plan and investigate the amount of energy given off by the burning of different crisps or biscuits. Predictions can be made on the basis of lists of ingredients on packaging.

Unit 7J ELECTRICAL CIRCUITS

The activities in this unit concern investigations into electrical current in a variety of contexts. The activities can be used to help pupils identify variables, make predictions, plan fair tests and identify and describe patterns in results.

1 a An ammeter.

b Length of wire.

c Current through the wire.

d As the length of the wire increases, the current through the wire decreases (or the inverse – as the length of the wire decreases, the current through the wire increases) *Or* The longer the wire, the lower the current (or the inverse – the shorter the wire, the higher the current).

2 a I think that as the number of bulbs increase, the *brightness of the bulbs will decrease.*

b Discuss pupils' answers – their explanations should relate to the idea that the energy carried by the electrical current is shared out between the bulbs. For example, 'I think that this will happen because, as the number of bulbs increases, the energy carried by the electrical current is shared out more and more'.

3 a As the voltage of the power pack increases, the current through the circuit increases (or the inverse – as the voltage of the power pack decreases, the current through the circuit decreases). *Or* The higher the voltage, the higher the current (or the inverse – the lower the voltage, the lower the current).

b Discuss pupils' answers. Explanations should relate to the idea that the voltage of the power pack represents the push that moves the electrical current around the circuit. For example, 'I think that this happens because the higher the voltage of the power pack, the greater the push given to the electrical current, making it flow around the circuit faster'.

4 a Pupils should be able to devise a plan in which electrical current, measured by an ammeter, is passed through a piece of wire immersed in a beaker of water. A reading is then taken of the temperature of the water after a given period of time. The experiment is repeated two more times with different amounts of current (produced by altering the settings on the voltmeter).

b Type of wire, length of wire, volume of water in beaker, starting temperature of water in the beaker, length of time given for the water to heat up.

5 a **i** material **ii** Amount of current flowing when connected to a 9 V battery.

b **i** Copper is used as the material for electrical wires because it allows electrical current to flow through it easily, i.e. because it is a good electrical conductor. **ii** Plastic is used to coat electrical wires because is does not allow electrical current to flow through it so preventing electrical shocks, i.e. because it is a good electrical insulator.

Extension – Plan and carry out an investigation into how the number of bulbs in a parallel circuit affects the current flowing through the circuit. Compare these results with those gained for series circuits.

Link – Exploring Science 7Jc

Unit 7K FORCES AND THEIR EFFECTS

The activities in this unit concern the measurement of forces and explore the link between force and motion. The activities can be used to help pupils plan fair tests, interpret and make predictions from tables and graphs and identify and describe patterns in data.

1 a How does the force on a spring affect its extension?

   b The units of Newtons for force.

   c 120 mm

   d Pupils should be able to identify the pattern in results where every additional unit of force leads to an extension of 40 mm.

2 a The shoes must be pulled over the same surface, at the same speed, with the same mass inside.

   b Any of the three shoes can be chosen as long at the explanation in part (c) is valid.

   c Trainer – has many large ridges so would be able to catch onto rough surfaces easily – there may also be comments on the type of material used which is designed to grip.

     Flat shoe – has a large surface area of the sole in contact with the surface which might make the levels of friction high.

     Stiletto-heeled shoe – the heel might dig down into certain surfaces and give a very good grip.

3 a 3 N

   b The reading on the forcemeter will go down.

   c This happens because the upthrust from the water cancels out some of the weight of the toy car.

4 a A–B: constant speed; B–C: stationary; C–D: constant speed; D–E: stationary.

   b A–B is a slower constant speed than C–D. This can be seen by the fact that the line A–B is not as steep as C–D.

5 a As the wetness of the road increases, the distance needed to stop a car increases (or the inverse – as the wetness of the road decreases, the distance needed to stop a car decreases) *Or* The wetter the road, the greater the distance needed to stop the car (or the inverse – the dryer the road, the shorter the distance needed to stop the car).

   b There is a minimum legal tread level for safety reasons. The less tread a tyre has, the greater the distance needed to stop the car.

Extension – Plan and carry out an investigation into which sort of material would allow a child to go down a slide the fastest.

    Link – Exploring Science 7Kd

Unit 7L THE SOLAR SYSTEM AND BEYOND

The activities in this unit concern the interpretation and explanation of planetary data. The activities can be used to help pupils make predictions, interpret tables and graphs, identify and describe relationships between variables and to form conclusions.

1 a As the distance from the Sun increases, the time to orbit the Sun increases (or the inverse – as the distance from the Sun decreases, the time to orbit the Sun decreases). *Or* The greater the distance from the Sun, the longer the time to orbit the Sun (or the inverse – the less the distance from the Sun, the shorter the time to complete one orbit of the Sun).

   b *Either* the greater the distance from the Sun, the slower the planets are moving, *or* the greater the distance from the Sun, the further the planets are having to travel to make one journey around the Sun.

2 a position C

   b 6 pm is 12 hours after 6 am. In this time the Earth would have spun exactly 180° of the way around its axis so the shadow will be 180° different as well.

3 a The shadow would be much longer.

   b During the winter months the UK is tilted at a greater angle away from the Sun than in the summer so all shadow lengths are longer.

Sc1 Skills for Key Stage 3 © Pearson Education Limited 2004

4 a As the mass of the planet increases, the size of the force of gravity increases (or the inverse – as the mass of the planet decreases, the size of the force of gravity decreases) *Or* The greater the mass of the planet, the greater the size of the force of gravity (or the inverse – the lower the mass of the planet, the lower the size of the force of gravity).

   b Any figure below 9. Mars has a smaller mass than Venus and the force of gravity on Venus is 9N/kg.

5 Graph A = shadow length as the length of the shadows decrease during the morning until reaching their shortest length at midday and then increasing in length again.

   Graph B = temperature as night-time temperatures in the summer remain quite high.

   Graph C = light intensity as this will start and end at very low levels and rise to a peak at midday.

Extension – Carry out research using the Internet to determine environmental conditions on different parts of the globe. Explain these differences using ideas of the Earth's tilt and rotation.

GRAPH QUESTIONS

Pupils could come up with a range of questions referring to any aspects of the graph on display. The examples below, whilst not exhaustive, act as a guide to the sorts of questions that pupils could suggest. See Skills progression chart on page vii for more information.

Variables:

Name the independent variable.

Name the dependent variable.

What is the question being investigated?

Say how you might have measured the independent and dependent variables.

Fair test:

Which things would have been kept the same to make this a fair test?

Graph presentation:

Can you see any mistakes or omissions on this graph?

Graph interpretation:

What is the value of the dependent variable when the independent variable is ...? (Or the inverse.)

As the independent variable rises, what happens to the dependent variable?

How does the independent variable affect the dependent variable? (Or the inverse.)

Can you see a pattern in these results?

At which point is the graph changing most rapidly? *Relating to the gradient of the graph.*

Graph prediction:

What do you think would happen to the shape of the graph if it were continued?

Anomalous results:

Which result(s) look anomalous?

What could have caused these anomalies?

What shape line of best fit would be used here?

Conclusions:

Explain why (state result or finding) has occurred.

Explain why this pattern has been found.

Evaluations:

How could the data on this graph be displayed in a better way? *For example, by changing the type of graph, altering the axes, drawing a line of best fit.*

How could more information for this graph be obtained? *For example, by altering the range/adding intermediate figures.*

TABLE QUESTIONS

Pupils could come up with a range of questions referring to any aspects of the table on display. The examples below, whilst not exhaustive, act as a guide to the sorts of questions that pupils could suggest. See Skills progression chart on page vii for more information.

Variables:

Name the independent variable.

Name the dependent variable.

What is the question being investigated?

Say how you might have measured the independent and dependent variables.

Fair test:

Which things would have been kept the same to make this a fair test?

Table presentation:

Can you see any mistakes or omissions on this table?

Can you suggest another way in which this data could be presented?

Table interpretation:

Which (state independent variable value) in the table has the largest/smallest (state dependent variable)?

How many times has this experiment been repeated?

Why has the experiment been repeated (insert number) times?

Are there any results on this table that look unlikely? Explain your answer to the above.

Conclusions:

What is the relationship between (state the independent variable) and (state the dependent variable)?

Can you see a pattern in these results?

Evaluations:

How could more information for this table be obtained? *For example, by altering the range/adding intermediate figures, repeating the investigation (more times).*

STARTER WORKSHEET

1 Investigating the action of amylase

Amylase is an enzyme that breaks down starch into glucose. Jack and Ellie wanted to find out how quickly this happened. They set up an experiment as shown below:

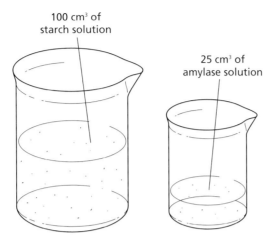

100 cm³ of starch solution

25 cm³ of amylase solution

Jack and Ellie started a stopwatch and after a period of time added the amylase enzyme.

The graph shows the results from their investigation:

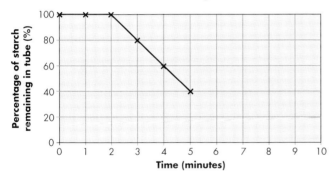

Effect of time on the digestion of starch.

a How many minutes into the investigation did Jack and Ellie add the amylase?

....

b Explain your answer to part (a).

....

....

c Predict when all of the starch will have been digested.

....

....

Link – Exploring Science 8Ad

STARTER WORKSHEET

2 Investigating the action of protease

Protease is an enzyme that breaks proteins down into amino acids. Chris and Jo wanted to investigate how the speed of the enzyme's action was affected by the temperature of the enzyme. Here are their results:

Temperature of protease solution (°C)	Time taken for protease to break protein down into amino acids (seconds)			
	Test 1	Test 2	Test 3	Average
20	370	345	362	359
25	290	280	300	290
30	220	105	212	179
35	100	110	90	100

Use the table to answer the following:

a Name the independent variable. ....

b Name the dependent variable. ....

c Describe the pattern that you can see between these variables.

....

....

STARTER WORKSHEET

3 Investigating the action of protease

Protease is an enzyme that breaks proteins down into amino acids. Chris and Jo wanted to investigate how the speed of the enzyme's action was affected by the temperature of the enzyme. Here are their results:

Temperature of protease solution (°C)	Time taken for protease to break protein down into amino acids (seconds)			
	Test 1	Test 2	Test 3	Average
20	370	345	362	359
25	290	280	300	290
30	220	105	212	179
35	100	110	90	100

a How many times was the investigation repeated at each temperature? ....

b Why are investigations repeated?

....

c Which result in the table looks unlikely (an anomalous result)? Explain your answer.

....

d What should Chris and Jo do with this anomalous result before trying to present the data in a graph or table?

....

STARTER WORKSHEET

4 Investigating the action of protease

Protease is an enzyme that breaks down proteins to amino acids. Chris and Jo wanted to investigate how the speed of the enzyme's action was affected by the temperature of the enzyme. Here are their results:

Temperature of protease solution (°C)	Time taken for protease to break protein down into amino acids (seconds)			
	Test 1	Test 2	Test 3	Average
20	370	345	362	359
25	290	280	300	290
30	220	105	212	179
35	100	110	90	100

a Sketch the outline of a graph presenting these results. You will need to decide:

  i   the type of graph to draw (e.g. bar graph or line graph)

  ii   the axes labels you will use

  iii the scales you will use.

b Explain your choices.

....

....

....

....

STARTER WORKSHEET

5 Investigating the action of amylase

Kunal and Tania want to investigate what affects how fast an enzyme called amylase will break down some starch into glucose.

a Make a list of all the possible variables that they could choose to investigate.

....

....

....

b Choose one variable from your list and complete the question that Kunal and Tania would be investigating:

Kunal and Tania want to find out how the ....

affects ....

c Which variables would Kunal and Tania have to keep the same to make the investigation fair?

....

....

Link – Exploring Science 8Ad

Sc1 Skills for Key Stage 3 © Pearson Education Limited 2004

STARTER WORKSHEET

1 Do growing peas respire?

Look at the diagram on the right.

The temperature in each test tube was measured over 12 hours and presented as a graph, shown below, on the right.

a What information is missing from the graph?

....

boiled peas   growing peas

b Which line on the graph represents the test tube with growing peas?

....

c Explain how you made this decision.

....

....

....

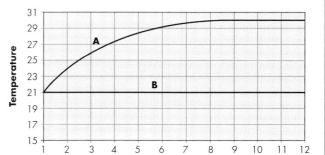

Link – Exploring Science 8Ba

Sc1 Skills for Key Stage 3 © Pearson Education Limited 2004

STARTER WORKSHEET

2 Investigating the effect of exercise on heart rate

Rashid and Monica wanted to investigate the effect of exercise on their heart rate. This is what they did:

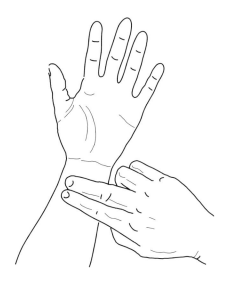

1   Both found the pulse in their wrist. They then counted the number of pulses in one minute whilst sitting down. They recorded this figure as their resting rate.

2   Each then took some exercise by stepping up and down from a PE bench.

3   They then measured their pulse rates again every minute until they returned to their resting rate.

a   Predict the effect that exercise would have had on the pulse rate of both pupils.

....

....

b   Explain why you think this would happen.

....

....

....

....

Rashid said that he must be fitter than Monica because his pulse rate returned to his resting rate quicker than hers. Monica disagreed, saying that the investigation was not fair.

c   Explain in what ways the investigation could have been unfair.

....

....

....

d   In what ways could the method of collecting data have been imprecise? Can you suggest how more precise data could have been obtained?

....

....

....

....

Link – Exploring Science 8Bb

STARTER WORKSHEET

3 Investigating the effect of different amounts of sugar on the respiration of yeast.

Yeast is a living organism. It respires by breaking down sugar which releases carbon dioxide gas. The diagrams show an investigation which was set up to find the effect of the amount of sugar available on the respiration of yeast.

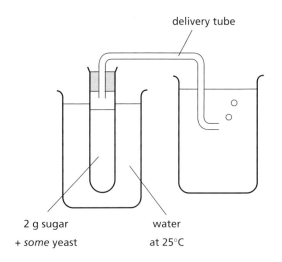

2 g sugar
+ *some* yeast

water
at 25°C

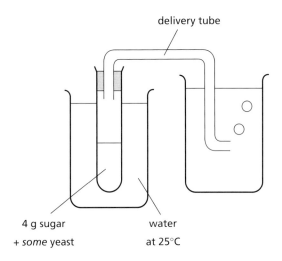

4 g sugar
+ *some* yeast

water
at 25°C

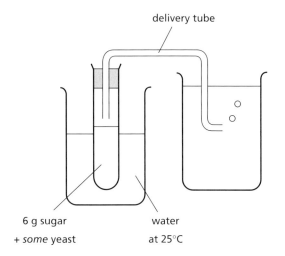

6 g sugar
+ *some* yeast

water
at 25°C

a In what ways is this investigation unfair?

....

....

....

b What changes would you make to ensure a fair investigation?

....

....

....

Link – Exploring Science 8Ba

Sc1 Skills for Key Stage 3 © Pearson Education Limited 2004

STARTER WORKSHEET

4 Investigating respiration in yeast

Yeast is a living organism. It respires by breaking down sugar which releases carbon dioxide gas. The diagram below shows an experiment which was set up to investigate the effect of temperature on the respiration of yeast and the table below shows the results recorded.

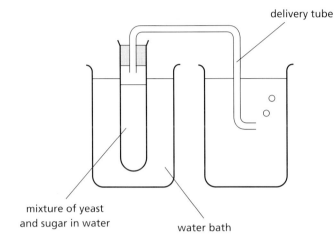

delivery tube

mixture of yeast and sugar in water

water bath

Temperature	Number of bubbles
10	2
20	6
30	12
40	12
50	1

a What is the question being investigated?

b What is wrong with the table?

c What would be the best type of graph to present this data? Explain your answer.

d How would you use this graph to make predictions of the number of bubbles produced at 25 °C?

Link – Exploring Science 8Ba

STARTER WORKSHEET

5 Investigating respiration in yeast

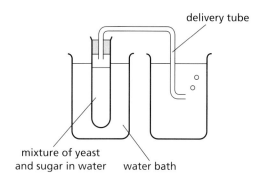

Yeast is a living organism. It respires by breaking down sugar which releases carbon dioxide gas. The diagram on the right shows how data was collected for an investigation into the effect of temperature on the respiration of yeast. The graph shows the results of this investigation.

a What information is missing from the graph?

....

b At what temperature is most respiration taking place?

....

c Explain why the number of bubbles gets less after this point.

....

....

....

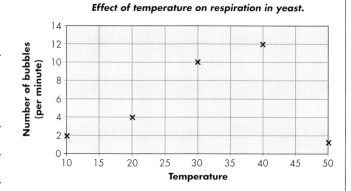

Effect of temperature on respiration in yeast.

Link – <u>Exploring Science 8Ba</u>

Sc1 Skills for Key Stage 3 © Pearson Education Limited 2004

STARTER WORKSHEET

1 Investigating bread dough

Tania and Danielle are investigating how high mixtures of bread dough rise. The results of their experiment after 30 minutes are shown on the right:

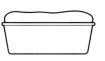

200 g flour
25 g yeast
50 g sugar

200 g flour
25 g yeast
100 g sugar

200 g flour
25 g yeast
150 g sugar

a What question are Tania and Danielle investigating?

....

....

Before the experiment Danielle made a prediction. When she looked at the results, she found that her prediction was correct.

b What was Danielle's prediction?

....

c Apart from the types and amounts of ingredients, what variables would Tania and Danielle have to control to keep the investigation fair?

....

....

Link – <u>Exploring Science 8Cb</u>

 Sc1 Skills for Key Stage 3 © Pearson Education Limited 2004

STARTER WORKSHEET

2 Investigating the effect of temperature on yeast

The graph on the right shows the changes in population of three samples of yeast kept at different temperatures.

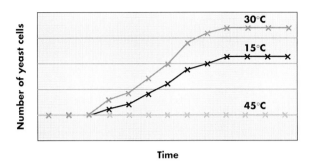

a Describe the change in population of the sample kept at 30 °C.

....

....

....

b Describe the change in population of the sample kept at 45 °C.

....

c Explain why the 45 °C line was different to the 30 °C line.

....

....

Link – Exploring Science 8Cb

Sc1 Skills for Key Stage 3 © Pearson Education Limited 2004

STARTER WORKSHEET

3 Response to infection

The information below describes the reaction of the human body to infection:

A – About 2 days after being infected by a bacterium, the human body starts to respond by producing antibodies.

B – The levels of antibodies in the blood increase for a few days until they reach a peak.

C – The levels drop off as the bacteria are destroyed.

D – At the end of the infection a small number of antibodies remain in the blood system.

Sketch a graph showing these changes in antibody levels over time. Label the line to show the sections A, B, C and D.

Link – Exploring Science 8Ce

Sc1 Skills for Key Stage 3 © Pearson Education Limited 2004

STARTER WORKSHEET

4 Investigating the action of antibiotics

Tim decided to investigate how effective four different antibiotics were at preventing bacterial growth. He took four Petri dishes, each containing some agar jelly which had been inoculated with bacteria. He placed discs containing equal quantities of each different antibiotic on the surface of the Petri dish before putting on the lid of the dish and sealing it with sellotape.

Tim left the Petri dish for three days and then looked at it again. The diagram below shows what had happened.

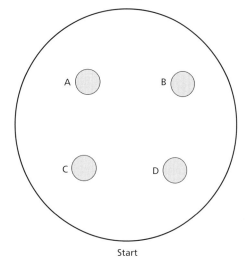

Start

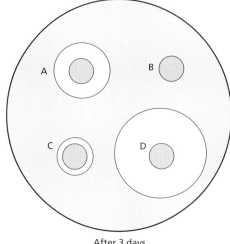

After 3 days

a Which antibiotic was the most effective at preventing bacterial growth?

....

b Explain your answer to part (a).

....

....

....

c Which antibiotic was the least effective at preventing bacterial growth?

....

d Explain your answer to part (c).

....

....

e What conditions would you recommend that the dish be kept in during the three days to maximise bacterial growth?

....

....

f Why was the dish sealed?

....

....

....

Link – Exploring Science 8Ce

Sc1 Skills for Key Stage 3 © Pearson Education Limited 2004

STARTER WORKSHEET

5   What happens to milk when it goes off?

Gurpreet was investigating what happened to milk when it went off. He predicted that the pH of the milk would get lower due to the waste products produced by bacteria in the milk. Gurpreet set up eight test tubes of milk and left them in an incubator at 25 °C. Each day he tested one of the samples using universal indicator.

Gurpreet plotted a graph from the investigation:

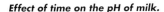

Effect of time on the pH of milk.

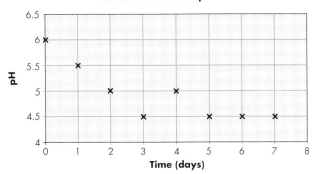

a   Which results in the graph support Gurpreet's prediction?

....

....

b   Which results do not support Gurpreet's prediction?

....

....

c   Which result on the graph looks unlikely?

....

....

d   Suggest why this result might have happened.

....

....

....

....

....

e   Predict how the results might have been different if the samples had been kept in a fridge at 5 °C.

....

....

f   Explain your answer to part (e).

....

....

STARTER WORKSHEET

1 Investigating bladder wrack

Bladder wrack is a type of seaweed found on the shores around Britain. The bladders are filled with air which allows the plant to float in the water so that it can absorb sunlight and make food.

Martin and Jackie carried out an investigation to see whether the number of bladders on the top 10 cm length of the seaweed varied depending on their locations. They investigated bladder wrack found on a very rocky coastline, one that was slightly rocky and one with no rocks. Their results are shown below:

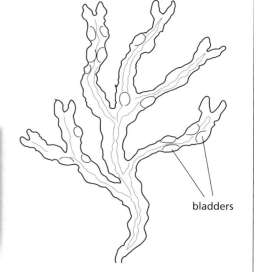

bladders

> Very rocky shore – 8, 7, 9, 10, 8
> Slightly rocky shore – 5, 7, 4, 6, 6
> Non rocky shore – 2, 3, 4, 3, 4

a Design a table to present all of these results.

b Design a table to display the average numbers of bladders (you will have to calculate these).

Link – Exploring Science 8Dc

Sc1 Skills for Key Stage 3 © Pearson Education Limited 2004

STARTER WORKSHEET

2 Investigating bladder wrack

Bladder wrack is a type of seaweed found on the shores around Britain. The bladders are filled with air which supports the plant in the water so that they can absorb sunlight and make food.

Martin and Jackie carried out an investigation to see whether the number of bladders on the top 10 cm length of the seaweed varied depending on their locations. They investigated bladder wrack found on a very rocky coastline, one that was slightly rocky and one with no rocks. Their results are shown in the graph:

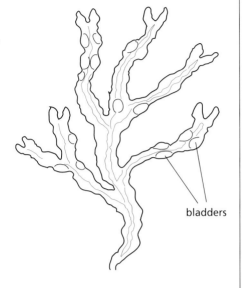

bladders

Effect of shoreline on average number of bladders.

Y-axis: Average number of bladders (10 cm)

X-axis: Type of shoreline — Very rocky (9), Slightly rocky (6), Non rocky (3)

a Describe the pattern that you can see in their results.

....

....

....

b The more rocky a shoreline is, the rougher the waves. Explain the pattern that you found in the bar graph.

....

....

....

....

Link – Exploring Science 8Dc

STARTER WORKSHEET

3 Investigating daisies on a school field

Rob and Annabel noticed that the daisies on their school field were not evenly distributed. In some areas there were far more than in others. They decided to try to find out why this was.

The diagram on the right shows you the section of the school field that Rob and Annabel decided to investigate.

a Make a list of the variables that they could have investigated.

....

....

b What measurements of the daisies would they have to make?

....

c Pick one variable and write out a question to be investigated.

....

Link – Exploring Science 8Dd

Sc1 Skills for Key Stage 3 © Pearson Education Limited 2004

STARTER WORKSHEET

4 Investigating daisies on a school field

Rob and Annabel wanted to investigate how the distance from a stream affected the numbers of daisies growing on their school field.

Rob and Annabel wanted to collect data to help with their investigation.

a What sampling method would you suggest they use?

....

....

b How could Rob and Annabel present their data?

....

....

Link – Exploring Science 8Dd

Sc1 Skills for Key Stage 3 © Pearson Education Limited 2004

STARTER WORKSHEET

5 Why does duckweed grow in some ponds but not others?

Duckweed is a type of plant that grows in canals, lakes and ponds. Alice noticed that the school pond was covered in duckweed whilst her pond at home had very little.
She decided to find out why there were these differences. She took some measurements from both ponds and compared the results.

duckweed

a What variables could Alice measure? ....
....

Alice took some measurements of the school pond one lunchtime and compared them to measurements taken that afternoon at her home.

b Alice's sister said that comparisons based on these readings would not be fair.
Explain why.

....

....

....

....

c How could Alice make a fairer comparison of the ponds?

....

....

....

....

Alice decided that one of the variables she would measure was the temperature of the water. She tried to use a thermometer but found it difficult to read in the bright sunlight.

d What piece of equipment could Alice use to make a more precise measurement of the temperature of water in the ponds?

....

STARTER WORKSHEET

1 Investigating conduction

Elizabeth wanted to find out which metal – iron, copper or lead, conducted heat energy the fastest. She took one rod of each metal and attached a drawing pin to the end of them with some wax. She then heated each rod with a Bunsen burner and timed how long it took for the heat to travel along the rod, melt the wax and cause the drawing pin to drop.

Philip said that Elizabeth's investigation was not fair.

a List all the ways in which Elizabeth's investigation was not fair.

iron

wax

Bunsen burner

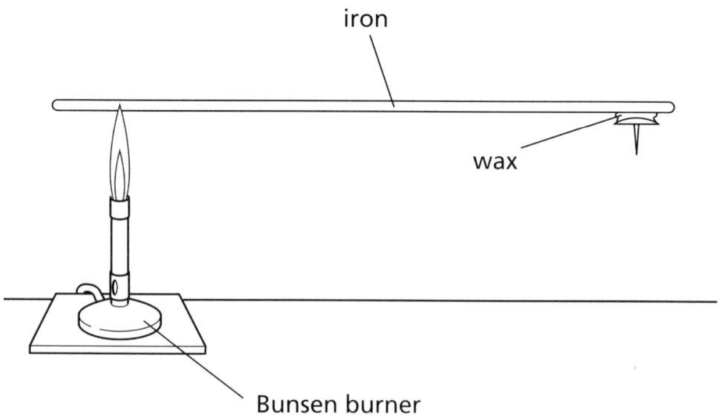

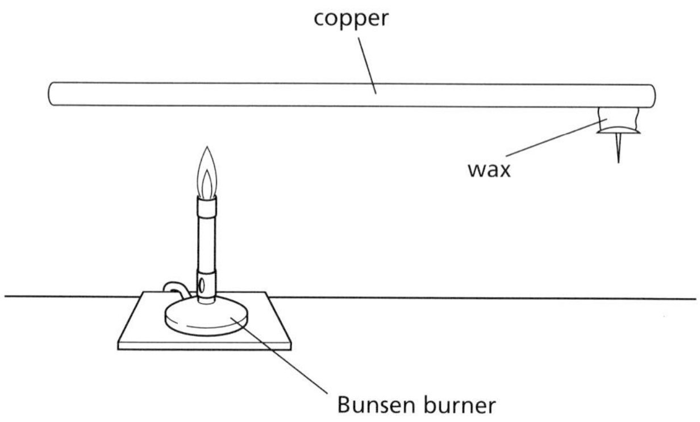

b Suggest how you could improve the investigation to make it fair.

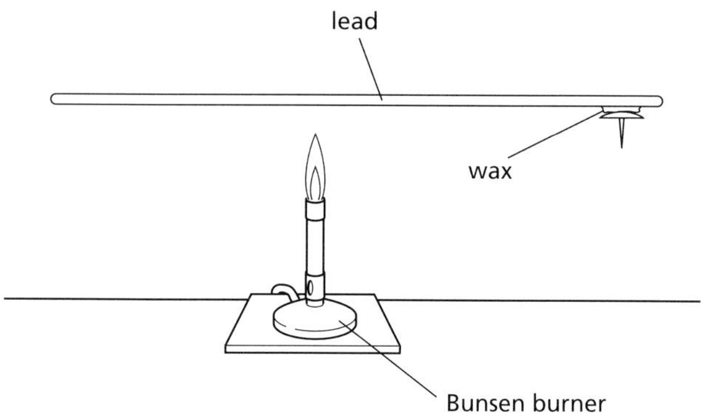

copper

wax

Bunsen burner

lead

wax

Bunsen burner

Link – Exploring Science 8Ec

STARTER WORKSHEET

2 Melting and boiling points

The table below shows data on the melting and boiling points of four different materials.

Material	Melting Point (°C)	Boiling Point (°C)
W	−200	−180
X	820	1340
Y	8	68
Z	−10	215

Use the information to answer the following questions:

a Which material has the highest melting point?

....

b Which material is a gas at 0 °C?

....

c What state would Y be at 21 °C?

....

STARTER WORKSHEET

3 Does heating copper affect its mass?

Ayala found that the mass of a piece of copper foil was 2.15 g.

She heated the foil strongly with a Bunsen burner to see whether the heat would affect the mass of the copper.

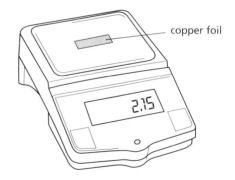

copper foil

a What safety precautions should Ayala have taken when heating the copper foil?

....

....

b What would you predict the mass of the copper foil to be after it has been heated?

☐ Less than 2.15 g   ☐ Still 2.15 g   ☐ More than 2.15 g

c Explain your answer to part (b).

....

....

STARTER WORKSHEET

4 What happens when calcium carbonate is heated?

Calcium carbonate is a compound of calcium, carbon and oxygen. When it is heated, carbon dioxide (an invisible gas) is given off, leaving calcium oxide. This is shown in the word equation below:

calcium carbonate → calcium oxide + carbon dioxide

a What equipment could you use to find out whether some mass had been lost from the calcium carbonate?

....

Anita was given a mystery powder and asked to try to find out whether it was an element or a compound. Using an electronic balance, she measured the mass of the powder as 0.58 g. Anita then heated the powder and measured the mass again. The mass after heating was still 0.58 g.

b Do the results suggest that the powder was an element or a compound?

....

c Do you think that there is enough evidence to decide the answer to this question? Explain your answer.

....

Link – Exploring Science 8Ed

✂ ....

STARTER WORKSHEET

5 Metals and non-metals

Greg and Krista are given some information about a mystery element.

conducts electricity?	yes
conducts heat?	yes
appearance	dull
texture	rough
melting point	1000 °C

Greg thinks that the element is a metal, but Krista thinks that it is a non-metal.

a What information in the table suggests that the element is a metal?

....

....

b What information in the table suggests that the element is a non-metal?

....

c What information in the table gives no help in deciding the nature of the element?

....

STARTER WORKSHEET

1 Interpreting graphs

Look at the graph on the right:

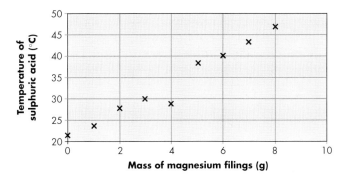

a Suggest a title for the graph. The title should make clear the information that is presented in the graph.

....

....

....

b Which shape 'line of best fit' would you use for these points?

☐ Best curve   ☐ Best straight line

Sachan said that one of the points plotted on the graph looked unlikely or anomalous.

c Write down the mass of magnesium filings that you think is an anomalous result. Explain your answer.

....

....

Sc1 Skills for Key Stage 3 © Pearson Education Limited 2004

STARTER WORKSHEET

2 Is apple juice really pure?

George wanted to find out whether a carton of pure apple juice bought from a supermarket really was pure, that is, made out of only one substance. He carried out the technique shown in the diagram on the right, below:

a What is the name of the technique shown in the picture?

☐ distillation ☐ filtering

☐ chromatography ☐ sieving

b Was the apple juice pure? ....

c Explain your answer to part (b).

....

....

....

....

....

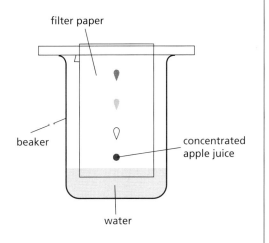

Link – Exploring Science 8Fd

Sc1 Skills for Key Stage 3 © Pearson Education Limited 2004

STARTER WORKSHEET

3 Investigating salt solutions

Different masses of common salt were dissolved in 250 cm³ of water. The salt solution was then heated to boiling point. The temperature of the solution was measured once it reached boiling point. The data obtained is presented in the graph.

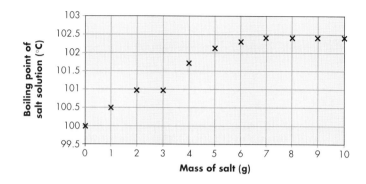

a An anomalous result seems to have occurred. Which mass of salt gave an anomalous result?

....

b What shape 'line of best fit' would you use for these points?

☐ Best curve
☐ Best straight line

c There came a point where adding more salt to the water stopped raising its boiling point.

i At what mass of salt did this happen? ....

ii Explain why this happened.

....

....

....

d Suggest the most precise way in which the temperature of the solution could be measured in this investigation.

....

....

Link – Exploring Science 8Fe

  Sc1 Skills for Key Stage 3 © Pearson Education Limited 2004

STARTER WORKSHEET

4 Investigating evaporation

Anya wanted to investigate the rate of evaporation of water. She took a beaker and filled it with 10 cm³ of water. She then placed the beaker in an oven at 20 °C for 1 hour. At the end of this time she measured the volume of water remaining.

Temperature of oven (°C)	Volume of water left in beaker after 1 hour (cm³)			
	Test 1	Test 2	Test 3	Average
20	10	10	10	10.0
40	9	6	10	8.3
60	8	8	8	8.0
80	6	6	5	5.7
100	2	1	0	1.0

Anya then repeated the investigation at four higher temperatures. Finally the whole procedure was repeated two more times. The table above shows the data Anya recorded.

a Name the independent variable. ....

b Name the dependent variable. ....

c Describe the pattern that you can see in these results.

....

....

d Predict the volume of water that would be left in the beaker if the temperature was 30 °C.

....

Sc1 Skills for Key Stage 3 © Pearson Education Limited 2004

STARTER WORKSHEET

5 Investigating evaporation

Anya wanted to investigate the rate of evaporation of water. She took a beaker and filled it with 10 cm³ of water. She then placed the beaker in an oven at 20 °C for 1 hour. At the end of this time she measured the volume of water remaining.

Temperature of oven (°C)	Volume of water left in beaker after 1 hour (cm³)			
	Test 1	Test 2	Test 3	Average
20	10	10	10	10.0
40	9	6	10	8.3
60	8	8	8	8.0
80	6	6	5	5.7
100	2	1	0	1.0

Anya then repeated the investigation at four higher temperatures. Finally the whole procedure was repeated a further two times. The table shows the data Anya recorded.

a This investigation was repeated three times for each temperature. Why is it a good idea to repeat investigations?

....

b Which result in the table looks unlikely (or anomalous)? ....

c Explain how you identified the anomalous result.

....

d Suggest how this unlikely result could have occurred.

....

Sc1 Skills for Key Stage 3 © Pearson Education Limited 2004

STARTER WORKSHEET

1 Investigating soil drainage

Plan a fair test to investigate the drainage properties of samples of sandy soil, clay soil and loam using the pieces of equipment shown below:

Include details on:

a the question being investigated

b the procedure you would follow

c the variables you would control to make the investigation fair.

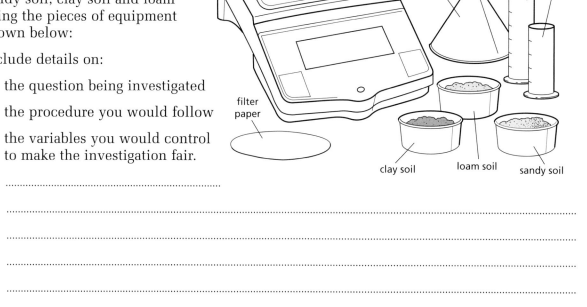

....

....

....

....

....

....

Link – <u>Exploring Science 8Ge</u>

Sc1 Skills for Key Stage 3 © Pearson Education Limited 2004

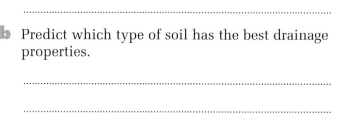

STARTER WORKSHEET

2 Comparing sandy and clay soils

Sandy soil is made up of large particles, whilst clay soil is made up of much smaller particles.

Look at the diagram on the right, showing an experiment carried out to compare the drainage properties of sandy soil and clay soil.

a In what ways is this investigation unfair?

....

....

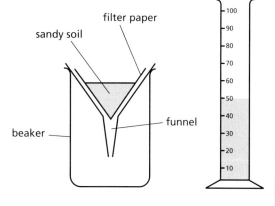

b Predict which type of soil has the best drainage properties.

....

....

c Explain how you made your prediction.

....

....

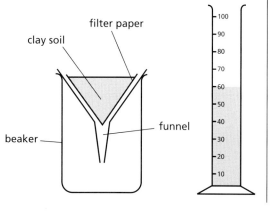

Sc1 Skills for Key Stage 3 © Pearson Education Limited 2004

STARTER WORKSHEET

3 Investigating the weathering of limestone

Pablo wanted to investigate the effect of the concentration of acid on the chemical weathering of limestone. He took six pieces of limestone, all with a mass of 5 g, and placed them into beakers containing 100 cm³ of varying concentrations of acid. He also took one 5 g piece of limestone and placed it in 100 cm³ of water. After 24 hours the limestone pieces were removed, dried and their new mass found.

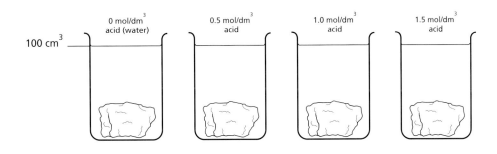

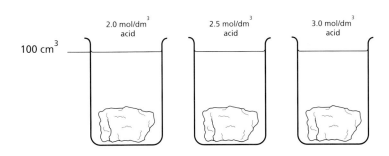

a Why was a control used?

....

....

b Which part of Pablo's investigation was a control?

....

....

c What do you predict the results of the investigation will be?

....

....

....

d Why did you make this prediction?

....

Link – Exploring Science 8Gb

STARTER WORKSHEET

4 Investigating the weathering of limestone

Pablo wanted to investigate the effect of the concentration of acid on the chemical weathering of limestone. He took six pieces of limestone, all with a mass of 5 g, and placed them into beakers containing 100 cm³ of varying concentrations of acid. He also took one 5 g piece of limestone and placed it in 100 cm³ of water. After 24 hours the limestone pieces were removed, dried and their new mass found. His results are shown on the graph:

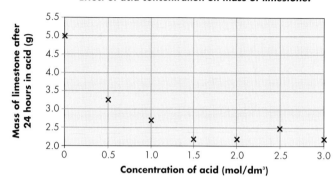

Effect of acid concentration on mass of limestone.

a Which shape 'line of best fit' would you use on this set of points?

☐ Best curve
☐ Best straight line

Pablo thought that one of the results may have been anomalous.

b At which concentration of acid did the anomalous result appear?

....

c What should Pablo do about this anomalous result?

....

....

....

Pablo had predicted that the stronger the acid, the less of the limestone would be remaining after 24 hours.

d Which points on the graph back up this prediction?

....

e Which points on the graph do not back up this prediction?

....

 Sc1 Skills for Key Stage 3 © Pearson Education Limited 2004

STARTER WORKSHEET

5 Investigating temperature and volume

Claudia took a sample of water and measured its volume at a range of different temperatures. Look at Claudia's data in the graph:

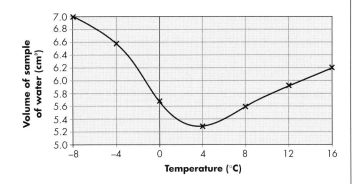

a Name the independent variable.

....

b Name the dependent variable.

....

c What is the question being asked in this investigation?

....

d At which temperature did the sample of water have the least volume?

....

Link – Exploring Science 8Gc

Sc1 Skills for Key Stage 3 © Pearson Education Limited 2004

STARTER WORKSHEET

1 Comparing granite and sandstone

Granite is a rock made out of interlocking grains, whilst sandstone has grains which are rounded.

Amy wanted to find out how porous to water granite was compared to sandstone. She took a piece of each rock and found their mass using an electronic balance. She then placed both in some water. A little later she took the rocks out of the water and weighed them again to see which had gained most mass.

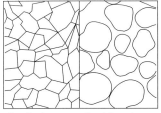

Granite has interlocking grains.

Sandstone has rounded grains.

a Which variables would Amy have to keep the same to make the investigation fair?

....

....

b Which type of rock do you predict would absorb the most water? ....

c Explain your reasons for your prediction.

....

....

Link – Exploring Science 8Hc

Sc1 Skills for Key Stage 3 © Pearson Education Limited 2004

STARTER WORKSHEET

2 Comparing granite and sandstone

Amy wanted to compare the porosity of granite and sandstone to water. She took similar sized pieces of each rock and found their mass using an electronic balance. Amy then placed both samples in some water. One hour later she took the rocks out of the water and weighed them again to see which had gained most mass. Here are her results:

Rock	Mass before	Mass after
granite	20	20
sandstone	20	28

a What information is missing from the table?

....

b Which rock was the most porous? Explain your answer.

....

....

c What kind of graph would be best suited to display this information?

....

Link – Exploring Science 8Hc

Sc1 Skills for Key Stage 3 © Pearson Education Limited 2004

✂ ....

STARTER WORKSHEET

3 Investigating different sandstones

Sandstone is a rock made out of rounded particles. It is described as being porous because there are gaps left between the rock particles through which water can flow.

Plan an investigation to compare the porosity of three different types of sandstone using the equipment shown in the diagram.

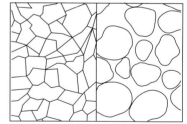

Granite has interlocking grains.

Sandstone has rounded grains.

Include details on:

a the procedure to be followed

b the variables you would have to keep the same to make the test fair.

....

....

....

....

....

....

....

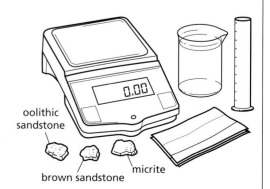

oolithic sandstone

brown sandstone

micrite

Link – Exploring Science 8Hc

Sc1 Skills for Key Stage 3 © Pearson Education Limited 2004

STARTER WORKSHEET

4 Investigating different limestones

There are many different types of limestone but all of them contain chemicals called carbonates. Carbonates react with acid to release carbon dioxide and water.

Look at the information in the table below:

Type of limestone	Volume of acid needed to completely react with the carbonate in 2 g samples of limestone (cm³)
oolithic	2.1
brown	3.4
micrite	1.6

a What size measuring cylinder would you use to measure these amounts of acid?

☐ 5 cm³ ☐ 10 cm³ ☐ 50 cm³

b Which rock contained the most carbonate?

....

c What type of graph could best be used to present these data?

....

Sc1 Skills for Key Stage 3 © Pearson Education Limited 2004

STARTER WORKSHEET

5 Modelling the formation of igneous rocks

Phenyl salicylate, or salol as it is more commonly known, is a chemical which can be used to model the formation of igneous rocks. When salol crystals cool to 42 °C after heating in a test tube, crystals form. The size of the crystals formed depends upon how quickly the salol cools.

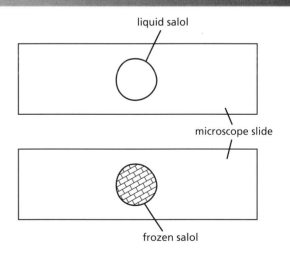

a What piece of equipment could you use to best observe the formation of salol crystals?

....

b How could you alter the rate at which the liquid salol cools and freezes?

....

c What pattern would you expect to find between the rate at which the liquid salol cools and the size of the crystals formed?

....

....

Sc1 Skills for Key Stage 3 © Pearson Education Limited 2004

STARTER WORKSHEET

1   Which material is best for hats?

Muriel and James had three winter hats. One was made out of cotton, one from polyester and one from wool.

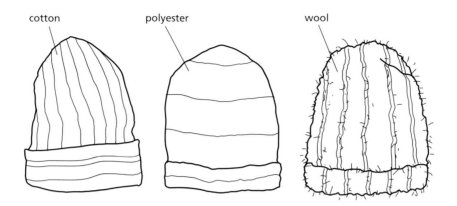

cotton   polyester   wool

They decided to find out which hat would keep their heads warmest on a winter walk.

Plan an investigation that Muriel and James could carry out to find out the answer to this question. Include details on:

a the procedure they could follow including a diagram of the apparatus used

b how they could keep the investigation fair.

....

....

....

....

....

....

....

....

Link – Exploring Science 8Id

STARTER WORKSHEET

2 Which material is best for hats?

Muriel and James had three winter hats. One was made out of cotton, one from polyester and one from wool. They decided to find out which hat would keep their heads warmest on a winter walk. They carried out the following plan:

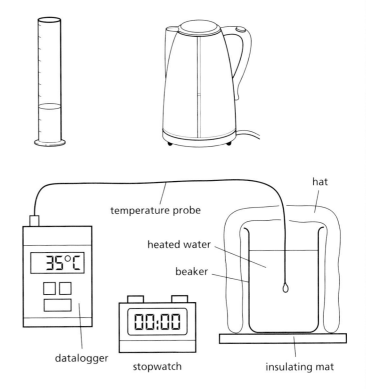

1 Measure out 100 cm³ of water using a 100 cm³ measuring cylinder.
2 Heat the water in a kettle until it boils.
3 When the water has cooled down to 70 °C add it to a beaker, put on the first hat and start a stopwatch.
4 Measure the temperature of the water in the beaker every 2 minutes until 10 minutes has passed using a datalogger with a temperature probe.
5 Repeat the investigation with another hat.

Muriel thought that the beaker should be cooled down with cold water after each investigation.

a Explain why Muriel thought this.

....

....

....

b What safety precautions should Muriel and James take?

....

....

....

James thought that the investigations should be repeated five times for each hat.

c Why is it a good idea to repeat results?

....

....

Link – Exploring Science 8Id

STARTER WORKSHEET

3 **Which is the best material for hats?**

Muriel and James had three winter hats. One was made out of cotton, one from polyester and one from wool. They decided to find out which hat would keep their heads warmest on a winter walk. On the right is a graph showing their results:

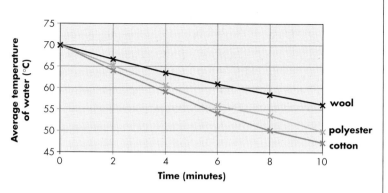

a Describe how the average temperature of the water changed with time when the polyester hat was on the beaker.

....

....

b Which hat kept the water hottest? ....

c What was the average temperature of the water after 8 minutes when the cotton hat was being used?

....

Link – Exploring Science 8Id

Sc1 Skills for Key Stage 3 © Pearson Education Limited 2004

STARTER WORKSHEET

4 **How does temperature affect footballs?**

Kieran and Titus carried out an investigation into the effect of temperature on the gas pressure inside a football. On the right is a graph to show their results:

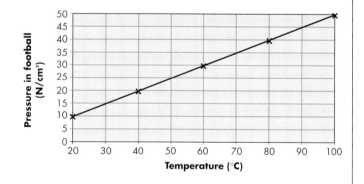

a Describe the pattern that you can see in these results.

....

....

b Explain why this pattern was found using the idea of particles.

....

....

c Predict the pressure in the football when the temperature is 50 °C. ....

Link – Exploring Science 8Ic

Sc1 Skills for Key Stage 3 © Pearson Education Limited 2004

STARTER WORKSHEET

5 Investigating heat transfer in metals

Abbey and Katya investigated how long heat took to travel through a 10 cm rod of metal. They took rods of equal thickness but made of different metals and placed one end in a Bunsen burner flame. They then timed how long it took for the temperature at the other end of the rod to rise by 10 °C.

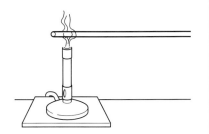

a Suggest a piece of equipment that would be able to accurately measure a 10 °C rise in the temperature of the end of the rods.

....

b Design a table for Abbey and Katya's results.

copper – 35 seconds

iron – 55 seconds

lead – 130 seconds

steel – 50 seconds

Link – Exploring Science 8Ib

Sc1 Skills for Key Stage 3 © Pearson Education Limited 2004

STARTER WORKSHEET

1 Investigating magnets

Georgina and Eleanor wanted to find out which of three magnets was the strongest. They investigated the magnets by finding out how many masses each magnet could support before they fell off. Here are the results of their investigations:

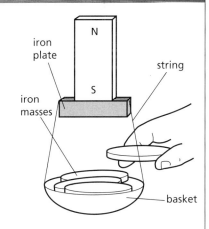

Magnet	Number of 1 g masses held before the basket fell
A	12
B	19
C	14

a Which was the strongest magnet? Explain your answer.

....

b Which was the weakest magnet? Explain your answer.

....

c In this investigation, name:

  i the dependent variable ....

  ii the independent variable. ....

Link – Exploring Science 8Ja

Sc1 Skills for Key Stage 3 © Pearson Education Limited 2004

STARTER WORKSHEET

2 Investigating electromagnets

Marcus was asked to find out what affects
the strength of electromagnets. He was given
a simple electromagnet made from a coil of
wire and a power supply.

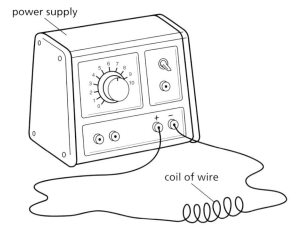

power supply

coil of wire

a What variables could Marcus investigate?

....

....

....

....

b Form a question for Marcus to investigate.

....

....

Link – Exploring Science 8Jd

Sc1 Skills for Key Stage 3 © Pearson Education Limited 2004

- -

STARTER WORKSHEET

3 Investigating electromagnets

Look at the information in the graph.

a Name:

   i   the independent variable

   ....

   ii the dependent variable.

   ....

Effect of number of coils on an electromagnet on the mass of iron that it can support.

(graph: x-axis "Number of coils on electromagnet" 0–30; y-axis "Mass of iron that could be supported by the electromagnet (g)" 0–60; points approx (5,10), (10,20), (15,18), (20,40), (25,50))

b Which shaped 'line of best fit'
would you use here?

   ☐ Best curve   ☐ Best straight line

c Comment on anything you noticed when you drew a line of best fit.

....

....

....

Link – Exploring Science 8Jd

Sc1 Skills for Key Stage 3 © Pearson Education Limited 2004

STARTER WORKSHEET

4 Investigating electromagnets

Look at the information in the graph.

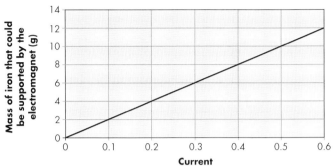

Effect of current on mass that could be supported by an electromagnet.

a What is missing from the graph?

....

....

....

b Describe the pattern that you can see between the current and the strength of the electromagnet.

....

....

....

Link – Exploring Science 8Jd

Sc1 Skills for Key Stage 3 © Pearson Education Limited 2004

- ✂

UNIT 8J **MAGNETS AND ELECTROMAGNETS**

STARTER WORKSHEET

5 Investigating electromagnets

Brian investigated the effect of varying the material of the core of an electromagnet on its ability to support a basket of weights. He noted down his results on a piece of paper.

a Present these results in a table, making sure that you use appropriate headings and units.

iron – 10 g
copper – 3 g
soft iron – 14 g
steel – 7 g

b Which material made the electromagnet the strongest?

....

Link – Exploring Science 8Jd

Sc1 Skills for Key Stage 3 © Pearson Education Limited 2004

STARTER WORKSHEET

1 Investigating reflection of light

Sketch a graph showing the relationship between the angle at which a ray of light hits a mirror (the angle of incidence) and the angle of the ray that is reflected (the angle of reflection). Make sure that:

a a suitable scale is used

b the axes are labelled

c units are included on the axes.

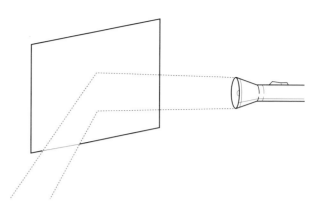

Link – <u>Exploring Science 8Kc</u>

✂ ....

STARTER WORKSHEET

1 Investigating reflection of light

Sketch a graph showing the relationship between the angle at which a ray of light hits a mirror (the angle of incidence) and the angle of the ray that is reflected (the angle of reflection). Make sure that:

a a suitable scale is used

b the axes are labelled

c units are included on the axes.

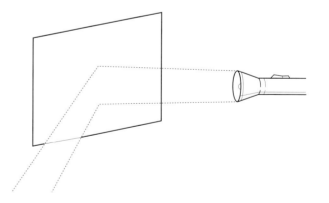

Link – <u>Exploring Science 8Kc</u>

STARTER WORKSHEET

2 Investigating refraction of light

Simon was investigating the way in which light changes direction when it moves from air into glass.

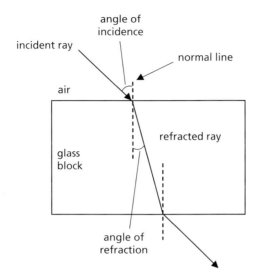

He set up the experiment shown in the diagram and measured the angle of incidence and angle of refraction. He then altered the angle of incidence of the light ray and measured the angles again. His results are shown in the table.

Angle of incidence	Angle of refraction
20	13
30	19
40	26
50	30

a What information is missing from Simon's table?

....

....

Simon looked at the results and tried to form a conclusion.

b Which of the following conclusions could Simon make from these results?

☐ *As the angle of incidence increases, the angle of refraction decreases*

☐ *The angle of refraction is always more than 5 degrees lower than the angle of incidence.*

☐ *The angle of incidence is always higher than the angle of refraction.*

Simon thought that some of his measurements may not have been very accurate.

c Is Simon's conclusion reliable? Explain your answer.

....

....

d Suggest why Simon's measurements may have been inaccurate.

....

....

Link – Exploring Science 8Kd

STARTER WORKSHEET

3 How far can light travel?

Look at the information in the table below:

Brightness of light (lux)	Distance over which light is visible (m)
200	240
400	370
600	500
800	630

a Name:

   i the dependent variable

   ....

   ii the independent variable.

   ....

b Describe the pattern that you can see in these results.

....

....

Link – Exploring Science 8Ka

✂ ....

STARTER WORKSHEET

4 How far can light travel?

a Sketch a graph that shows the relationship between the distance the light from a lighthouse can be seen and the amount of fog that there is. Think about:

   i which the independent variable is

   ii which the dependent variable is.

b Name a suitable piece of equipment that could be used to measure the strength of a light.

....

STARTER WORKSHEET

5 Splitting white light into colours

White light is made up of all the colours of the spectrum. When white light is viewed through a red filter only the red part of the light is able to travel through to the eye. The other colours are absorbed by the filter.

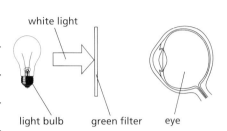

a Predict what you would see when white light is viewed through a green filter. Explain how you made your prediction.

....

....

....

....

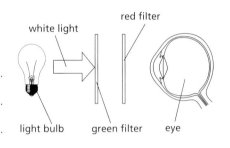

b What do you predict would be seen if a white light was viewed through a red filter placed on top of a green filter? Explain how you made your prediction.

....

....

....

Sc1 Skills for Key Stage 3 © Pearson Education Limited 2004

- ✂

STARTER WORKSHEET

1 Investigating sound

Nicky took a ticking clock and wrapped it in one layer of bubble wrap. She then measured the volume of the ticking that could be heard from a distance of 1 m. Nicky then repeated the investigation with two and then three layers of bubble wrap.

a What question was Nicky investigating?

....

....

b What do you predict the results of this investigation would be?

....

....

c Suggest the best piece of equipment to measure the volume of the ticking.

....

Link – Exploring Science 8Le

Sc1 Skills for Key Stage 3 © Pearson Education Limited 2004

STARTER WORKSHEET

2 Investigating sound

Nicky took a ticking clock and wrapped it in one layer of bubble wrap. She then measured the volume of the ticking that could be heard from a distance of 1 m. Nicky then repeated the investigation with two and then three layers of bubble wrap.

a List the variables that would have to be controlled to make the investigation fair.

....

....

....

....

....

Fiona said that the whole investigation should be repeated five times.

b Why should investigations be repeated?

....

Link – Exploring Science 8Le

Sc1 Skills for Key Stage 3 © Pearson Education Limited 2004

STARTER WORKSHEET

3 Interpreting graphs

Look at the information on the graph on the right:

a What information is missing from the graph?

....

....

....

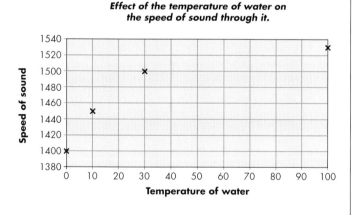

Effect of the temperature of water on the speed of sound through it.

b Which shape 'line of best fit' would you use here?

☐ Best curve ☐ Best straight line

c Describe the pattern that you can see in the results. ....

....

....

d Predict the speed of sound at 50 °C. ....

Link – Exploring Science 8Le

Sc1 Skills for Key Stage 3 © Pearson Education Limited 2004

STARTER WORKSHEET

4 How does age affect hearing?

Mike wanted to investigate the effect of the age of a person on the highest frequency note that they could hear. He selected four people of different ages. He tested their ability to hear high-frequency sounds using a signal generator and loudspeaker.

Mike predicted that the older a person was, the higher the note they would be able to hear. His results hare shown on the right.

Age of person (years)	Highest frequency note that can be heard when sitting 1 m from the loudspeaker (KHz)
13	20.0
25	17.5
50	18.0
75	15.0

a Did the data agree with Mike's prediction? Explain your answer.

....

....

b John said that Mike's investigation was unfair. Explain why John was right to say this.

....

....

....

....

Link – Exploring Science 8Ld

Sc1 Skills for Key Stage 3 © Pearson Education Limited 2004

✂

STARTER WORKSHEET

5 Investigating sound

Look at the information in the table below:

Density of material (kg/m³)	Speed of sound (m/s)
1	1500
2	3000
3	
4	6000

a State the question that is being investigated.

....

b Describe the pattern that you can see in these results.

....

....

....

c Predict the speed of sound when the density of the material is 3 kg/m³.

....

Link – Exploring Science 8Lc

Sc1 Skills for Key Stage 3 © Pearson Education Limited 2004

93

STARTER **THINKING SKILLS**

Look at the graph. What does it tell us?

....

....

....

....

....

Graphs help us to answer questions and see
patterns in results. What questions could you
ask about this graph that other people in your
class could answer?

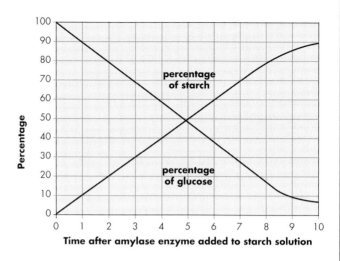

....

....

....

Sc1 Skills for Key Stage 3 © Pearson Education Limited 2004

STARTER **THINKING SKILLS**

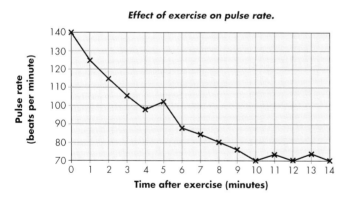

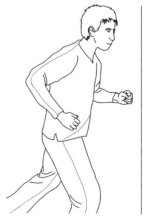

Look at the graph. What does it tell us?

....

Graphs help us to answer questions and see patterns in results. What questions could you ask
about this graph that other people in your class could answer?

....

....

....

Sc1 Skills for Key Stage 3 © Pearson Education Limited 2004

STARTER **THINKING SKILLS**

Mass of sugar in dough (g)	Height dough rose after 15 minutes (cm)			
	Test 1	Test 2	Test 3	Average
5	1.2	1.1	1.4	1.2
10	2.1	2.4	2.3	2.3
15	3.4	3.7	3.6	3.6
20	4.5	2.1	4.7	3.8
25	5.6	5.4	5.5	5.5

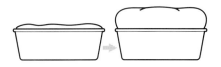

Look at the table. What does it tell us?

....

....

Tables present data and help us to answer questions and see patterns in results. What questions could you ask about this table that other people in your class could answer?

....

....

....

Sc1 Skills for Key Stage 3 © Pearson Education Limited 2004

STARTER **THINKING SKILLS**

Amount of oxygen in water (%)	Number of water fleas captured in 100 cm³ of water			
	1	2	3	Average
0	16	20	18	18
5	14	13	15	14
10	10	11	9	10
15	3	2	1	2
20	0	0	0	0

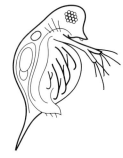

Look at the table. What does it tell us?

....

....

Tables present data and help us to answer questions and see patterns in results. What questions could you ask about this table that other people in your class could answer?

....

....

....

Sc1 Skills for Key Stage 3 © Pearson Education Limited 2004

STARTER **THINKING SKILLS**

Length of copper wire (mm)	Current flowing through wire when connected to a 1.5 volt battery (amps)			
	Test 1	Test 2	Test 3	Average
10	1.56	1.52	1.32	1.47
20	1.32	1.31	1.28	1.30
30	1.10	1.14	1.12	1.12
40	0.94	0.91	0.95	0.93
50	0.78	0.77	0.76	0.77

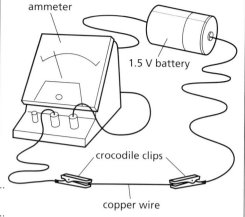

Look at the table. What does it tell us?

....

....

Tables present data and help us to answer questions and see patterns in results. What questions could you ask about this table that other people in your class could answer?

....

....

....

Sc1 Skills for Key Stage 3 © Pearson Education Limited 2004

✂ ••

STARTER **THINKING SKILLS**

Look at the graph. What does it tell us?

....

....

....

....

....

....

Effect of mass of salt in water on melting point of the solution.

Graphs help us to answer questions and see patterns in results. What questions could you ask about this graph that other people in your class could answer?

....

....

....

Sc1 Skills for Key Stage 3 © Pearson Education Limited 2004

STARTER **THINKING SKILLS**

Rock	Amount of water absorbed by a 10 g sample of rock (cm³)		
	Test 1	Test 2	Test 3
sandstone	6	4	5
limestone	8	7	8
chalk	4	3	9

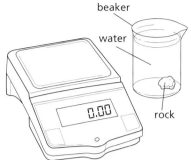

beaker

water

rock

Look at the table. What does it tell us?

....

Graphs help us to answer questions and see patterns in results. What questions could you ask about this graph that other people in your class could answer?

....

....

....

Sc1 Skills for Key Stage 3 © Pearson Education Limited 2004

STARTER **THINKING SKILLS**

Look at the graph. What does it tell us?

....

....

....

....

....

....

Effect of temperature of microscope slide on the size of salol crystals.

Average size of salol crystals formed when molten salol freezes (mm)

Temperature of microscope slide (°C)

Graphs help us to answer questions and see patterns in results. What questions could you ask about this graph that other people in your class could answer?

....

....

....

Sc1 Skills for Key Stage 3 © Pearson Education Limited 2004

STARTER **THINKING SKILLS**

Surface of tin containing 100 cm³ of water at 20 °C	Temperature of water in tin after 15 minutes heating with an infra-red lamp (°C)			
	Test 1	Test 2	Test 3	Average
shiny	24	22	32	26
black	42	40	44	42
white	28	30	29	29

Look at the table. What does it tell us?

....

....

Tables present data and help us to answer questions and see patterns in results. What questions could you ask about this table that other people in your class could answer?

....

....

....

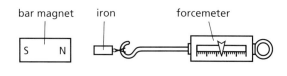

infra-red heater

thermometer

shiny tin

black tin

white tin

Sc1 Skills for Key Stage 3 © Pearson Education Limited 2004

✂ ....

STARTER **THINKING SKILLS**

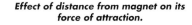

Effect of distance from magnet on its force of attraction.

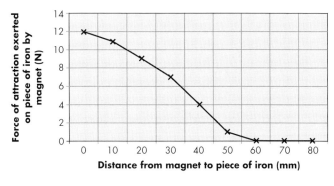

bar magnet   iron   forcemeter

Look at the graph. What does it tell us?

....

Graphs help us to answer questions and see patterns in results. What questions could you ask about this graph that other people in your class could answer?

....

....

....

Sc1 Skills for Key Stage 3 © Pearson Education Limited 2004

STARTER **THINKING SKILLS**

Brightness of light illuminating the clockface of Big Ben (lux)	Distance from which the clockface is visible on a foggy night (m)
1000	35
2000	60
3000	85
4000	110
5000	135

Look at the table. What does it tell us?

....

....

Tables present data and help us to answer questions and see patterns in results. What questions could you ask about this table that other people in your class could answer?

....

....

....

Sc1 Skills for Key Stage 3 © Pearson Education Limited 2004

STARTER **THINKING SKILLS**

Look at the graph. What does it tell us?

....

....

....

....

....

....

Effect of temperature of water on the speed of sound.

Graphs help us to answer questions and see patterns in results. What questions could you ask about this graph that other people in your class could answer?

....

....

....

Sc1 Skills for Key Stage 3 © Pearson Education Limited 2004

Unit 8A **FOOD AND DIGESTION**

The activities in this unit concern the digestion of food molecules by enzymes. The activities can be used to help pupils identify variables, plan fair tests, interpret information in tables and graphs and form conclusions.

1 a 2 minutes.

   b This is the point in the graph when the percentage of starch begins to drop, indicating that the amylase has been added.

   c 7 minutes – found through extrapolating the graph onwards until it reaches the *x*-axis.

2 a Temperature of the protease solution.

   b Time taken for protease to break down a protein solution to amino acids.

   c As the temperature increases, the time taken for protease to break down a protein solution into amino acids decreases (or the inverse – as the temperature decreases, the time taken for protease to break down a protein solution into amino acids increases) *Or* The higher the temperature, the shorter the time taken for protease to break down a protein solution into amino acids (or the inverse – the lower the temperature, the longer the time taken for protease to break down a protein solution into amino acids).

3 a Three times.

   b So that results can be compared against each other to check for reliability of data and to identify anomalous results.

   c Test 2 at 30 °C. This can be identified because it varies so greatly from the other results gained at 30 °C.

   d Repeat the 30 °C reading once more and use this figure in the calculation of an average instead of the anomalous result.

4 a and b

   i A line graph should be chosen as the results form continuous data. **ii** *x*-axis = Temperature of protease solution (°C) as this is the independent variable; *y*-axis = Time for protease to break down a protein solution into amino acids (seconds) as this is the dependent variable. **iii** *x*-axis scale: 20 to 35 in divisions of 5 as this fits the temperature measurements; *y*-axis scale: 90 or 100 to 360 in divisions of 10 as this matches the range of times recorded.

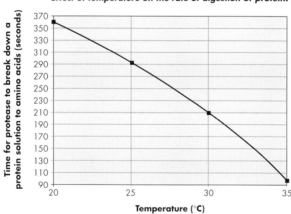

Effect of temperature on the rate of digestion of protein.

5 a Temperature, concentration or volume of starch solution, concentration or volume of amylase solution, pH of solution.

   b For example, 'Kunal and Tania want to find out how the *temperature of starch solution* affects *the speed at which amylase will break down starch solution into glucose*'.

   c All of the variables identified in (a) above except the variable chosen to be investigated.

Extension – Plan and carry out investigations into the action of biological washing powders (those containing enzymes) and non-biological ones.

Unit 8B **RESPIRATION**

The activities in this unit concern the process of respiration in animals, plants and fungi. Several questions centre around an investigation into the respiration of yeast. The activities can be used to help pupils identify variables, make predictions, plan and evaluate fair tests, identify patterns in results and form conclusions.

1 a The units are missing – you could ask pupils to suggest appropriate units (°C and hours). The lines should be labelled to indicate which pea type is which.

   b Line A, which levels off at 30 °C, represents the growing peas.

   c The peas are respiring to release energy to grow. Some energy is also released as heat.

2 a Increase in pulse rate.

   b Exercise increases muscles' requirements for oxygen. Consequently the heart has to beat faster to increase the supply of oxygenated blood.

   c Amount of exercise taken may have varied (that is, pupils may be of different masses and therefore expend different levels of energy when stepping on and off the bench), amount of steps completed may have varied, the time spent exercising may have varied.

   d Discuss inaccuracies of measuring pulse rate on the wrist. More accurate data could have been obtained using a heart monitor and datalogger.

3 a Varying volumes of yeast, varying thickness of delivery tubes leading to variation in the volume of carbon dioxide in the bubbles, varying volumes of water in water baths surrounding the test tubes.

   b Equal volumes of yeast, equal thickness of delivery tubes, equal volumes of water in water baths.

4 a How does temperature affect the number of bubbles of carbon dioxide produced by respiring yeast?

   b The table is missing units and the heading 'number of bubbles' should be made more specific, e.g. 'number of bubbles of carbon dioxide'.

   c A line graph as it is continuous data which can be plotted along a numbered x-axis.

   d Draw a line vertically up from 25 °C on the x-axis until it meets the plotted line. At this point draw a line horizontally until the y-axis is reached. Read off the number of bubbles from the scale.

5 a Units missing from x-axis.

   b 40 °C

   c The number of bubbles drops due to the denaturing (destruction) of the yeast enzymes responsible for carrying out respiration. Credit should be given if pupils suggest that the yeast has been killed by the high temperature.

Extension – Plan and carry out an investigation into the effect of exercise on breathing rate.

   Link – Exploring Science 8Bd

Unit 8C **MICROBES AND DISEASE**

The activities in this unit concern the factors affecting population sizes of organisms and the impact of bacteria on health. The activities can be used to help pupils identify variables, plan and evaluate fair tests, interpret and present information in graphs and to identify and explain anomalous results.

1 a How does the amount of sugar affect the height that bread dough rises in 30 minutes?

   b I think that as the amount of sugar increases, the height of the bread dough after 30 minutes will increase.

   c The temperature of the room in which the doughs were left, the type and volume of tin used.

2 a The population remained constant initially then rose rapidly until it reached a higher constant level.

   b The population remained constant throughout the experiment.

   c The temperature of 45 °C was too high for the yeast to survive so no reproduction took place.

3

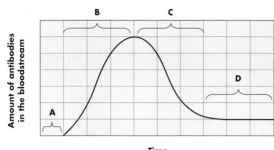

4 a D

b D had the largest area of inhibition of bacterial growth on the Petri dish.

c B

d B had no area of inhibition of bacterial growth.

e Kept in an incubator at approximately 35 °C.

f To prevent any health and safety risks associated with the release of bacteria into the environment.

5 a Days 0–3.

b Days 4–7.

c Day 4.

d Inaccuracies of readings. Universal indicator solution may have been contaminated or misinterpreted, datalogger measuring pH may have been incorrectly calibrated.

e The pH of the milk would not have dropped as quickly.

f Bacterial reproduction and respiration are slowed down by low temperatures.

Extension – Plan and carry out investigations into the variables affecting the rising of bread dough.

Link – Exploring Science 8Cb

Unit 8D ECOLOGICAL RELATIONSHIPS

The activities in this unit concern investigations into the growth and form of organisms in their natural environment. The activities can be used to give pupils opportunities to identify variables, plan fair tests using sampling techniques, give maximum attention to accuracy of measurement and reliability of data and to present and interpret data.

1 a

Type of shore	Number of bladders on the top 10 cm length of bladder wrack				
	Test 1	Test 2	Test 3	Test 4	Test 5
very rocky	8	7	9	10	8
slightly rocky	5	7	4	6	6
non-rocky	2	3	4	3	4

b

Type of shore	Average number of bladders on the top 10 cm length of bladder wrack
very rocky	8.4
slightly rocky	5.6
non-rocky	3.2

2 a As the number of rocks on the shoreline increased, the number of bladders on the top 10 cm of bladder wrack increased, (or the inverse – as the number of rocks on the shoreline decreased, the number of bladders on the top 10 cm of bladder wrack decreased). *Or* The rockier the shoreline, the more bladders were found on the top 10 cm of bladder wrack (or the inverse – the less rocky the shoreline, the less bladders were found on the top 10 cm of bladder wrack).

b The rockier the shoreline, the rougher the waves were and so the more bladders were needed to support the bladder wrack so that they could absorb sunlight and make food.

3 a The distance of the daisies from the stream, the light intensity, the temperature, the usage of the different areas (i.e. some areas might be used for sports more than other areas).

b The number of daisies in a certain area – they could use a quadrat for example.

    c   How does the distance from the stream affect the average number of daisies in the area of a quadrat? *Or* How does the light intensity affect the average number of daisies in the area of a quadrat? *Or* How does the usage of the ground affect the average number of daisies in the area of a quadrat?

4 a   The use of quadrats either in random sampling of areas or in the form of a line transect from the stream into the field.

    b   As a table, bar graph or line graph.

5 a   Temperature of the water, light intensity, pH of the water, oxygen levels of the water.

    b   The measurements would have had to be taken at the same time of day on the same day to allow them to be compared with each other.

    c   Use of a datalogger to measure conditions in the ponds over the same time period.

    d   Use a digital thermometer or temperature probe linked to a datalogger.

Extension – Conduct a survey of a local environment taking measurements of environmental conditions using dataloggers and probes. Investigate whether there is a link between the amount of light and temperature in different environments.

    Link – Exploring Science 8Dc

Unit 8E ATOMS AND ELEMENTS
The activities in this unit concern the properties of materials and observations of chemical reactions. The activities can be used to help pupils make predictions, select appropriate equipment, evaluate fair tests and interpret data in the form of tables and graphs.

1 a   Different lengths of rods, different thickness of rods, different amounts of wax fixing drawing pin, different positions of Bunsen burner along rod, different distances of Bunsen burner from rod, different sizes of Bunsen burner flame.

    b   Suggestions may well include heating all three rods simultaneously with the same Bunsen burner flame, using rods of the same thickness, same amount of wax, same type of flame. It may also be suggested that an alternative method of measuring the speed of heat transfer be used, for example, using heat-sensitive paper or temperature probes attached to the ends of each rod.

2 a   X

    b   W

    c   liquid

3 a   Wearing safety glasses, holding the copper foil in tongs, tying any long hair back.

    b   More than 2.15 g.

    c   The oxygen in the air has combined with the copper to form copper oxide, so increasing the mass of the foil.

4 a   An electronic balance.

    b   Element (using the previous example as a guide – that is, the compound calcium carbonate gave off carbon dioxide when heated and so reduced in mass, the mystery powder did not reduce in mass).

    c   There is insufficient evidence as some compounds do not decompose with heat.

5 a   Conducts electricity and heat and has a high melting point.

    b   Dull appearance.

    c   Rough texture.

Extension – Plan and carry out an investigation into the change in mass when burning magnesium.

    Link Exploring Science 8Ee

Unit 8F   COMPOUNDS AND MIXTURES

The activities in this unit concern mainly interpretative questions on the subject of mixtures of materials. The activities can be used to help pupils identify questions, interpret tables and graphs and suggest the shapes of lines of best fit, identify anomalous results and suggest causes.

1   a   The effect of the mass of magnesium filings on the temperature of sulphuric acid when they are mixed together.

   b   Best straight line.

   c   4 g because it is not close to the line of best fit; the temperature reading is too low.

   d   Use a datalogger and temperature probe.

2   a   chromatography

   b   no

   c   There were three different chemicals clearly visible on the chromatogram, showing that the apple juice was made of at least three different chemicals mixed together.

3   a   3 g

   b   Best curve.

   c   **i** 7 g **ii** The solution had become saturated so no more salt could be dissolved in the water.

4   a   Temperature of the oven.

   b   Volume of water left in the beaker after 1 hour.

   c   As the temperature of the oven increased, the volume of water left in the beaker after 1 hour decreased (or the inverse – as the temperature of the oven decreased, the volume of water left in the beaker after 1 hour increased). *Or* The hotter the oven, the smaller the volume of water left in the beaker after 1 hour (or the inverse – the cooler the oven, the larger the volume of water left in the beaker after 1 hour).

   d   Any number between 8.3 cm³ and 10 cm³.

5   a   To check the reliability of results, to check for anomalies.

   b   Test 2 for 40 °C.

   c   This figure is significantly different from the others in the series.

   d   Any from, incorrect temperature in oven, inaccurate measurement of water in beaker at start or end of investigation, incorrect timing.

Extension – Plan and carry out an investigation into the effect of the amount of dissolved salt on the boiling point of water with emphasis upon how the results can be made fair and reliable.

    Link – Exploring Science 8Fe

Unit 8G   ROCKS AND WEATHERING

The activities in this unit concern the structure and properties of common rocks and soils. The activities can be used to help pupils identify variables, make predictions, plan and evaluate fair tests and interpret graphs. Pupils are also asked to suggest the shapes of lines of best fit, identify anomalous results and give reasons for their occurrence.

1   a   How does the type of soil affect the drainage of water through the soil?

   b   Measure out a set mass of soil using an electronic balance. Place the soil into a cone of filter paper within a funnel. Add a set volume of water to the soil. Measure the volume of water that filters through in a given time period.

   c   The investigations should involve equal masses of the soils, equal volumes of water, equal times for drainage to occur and similar equipment.

2   a   Different volumes of soil, different amounts of water used.

   b   The sandy soil will have the best drainage properties.

   c   The larger particles making up the sandy soil will mean that there are larger gaps between particles for water to drain through.

3   a   To show that it was the acid that was responsible for the chemical weathering of the limestone.

   b   The piece of limestone that was placed in the water.

    c   Most pupils will write something like 'As the concentration of the acid increases, the mass of limestone remaining will decrease.' or 'The stronger the acid, the less limestone will be left.' However, credit can be given to alternatives where they are backed up with adequate explanations for part (d).

    d   The stronger the acid, the faster or greater the reaction between the acid and the limestone.

4 a   Best curve.

    b   2.5 mol/dm^3

    c   Repeat the investigation for this concentration and use this in his data instead.

    d   The range from 0 to 1.5 mol/dm^3.

    e   The range from 1.5 to 3.0 mol/dm^3.

5 a   temperature

    b   Volume of a sample of water.

    c   How does temperature affect the volume of a sample of water?

    d   4 °C

Extension – Plan and carry out an investigation into how porous different types of rock are.

    Link – Exploring Science 8Ga

Unit 8H **THE ROCK CYCLE**
The activities in this unit concern the properties of rocks and how these can be investigated. The activities can be used to help pupils make predictions, plan fair tests using appropriate equipment and interpret tables.

1 a   Rock samples should be of equal mass (and preferably equivalent shape to avoid differences in surface area), amount of water samples were put into, temperature of water, length of time rocks left submerged.

    b   sandstone

    c   Sandstone has rounded grains with gaps in between them allowing water to enter, whereas granite has interlocking grains leaving no room for the absorption of water.

2 a   Units (g) for measurements of mass.

    b   Sandstone as it showed a gain in mass.

    c   A bar graph.

3 a   This investigation could be planned in a variety of ways. Pupils may find the mass of each piece of rock, immerse the rocks in water for a set period of time and then find the mass again. The difference in gain of mass would indicate the porosity of the rock. More advanced pupils may suggest the calculation of a percentage gain in water to negate the impact of variation in the original mass of the rocks.

    b   Mass of rocks, shape or surface area of rocks, volume of water, time rocks immersed in water for.

4 a   5 cm^3

    b   Brown limestone.

    c   A bar graph.

5 a   microscope

    b   Use microscope slides that have been cooled or warmed (e.g. by placing them in a fridge/freezer or warm oven) to various temperatures before the liquid salol is added.

    c   As the rate of cooling increases, the size of the crystals decreases (or the inverse – as the rate of cooling decreases, the size of the crystals increases). *Or* The quicker the cooling, the smaller the crystals (or the inverse – the slower the cooling, the larger the crystals).

Extension – Plan and carry out an investigation to determine the amount of carbonate contained in a variety of different rocks.

    Link – Exploring Science 8Hb

Unit 8I HEATING AND COOLING

The activities in this unit concern the movement of heat energy and the effects of heat on pressure. The activities can be used to help pupils plan fair tests in which appropriate equipment is selected and reliable data obtained, interpret tables and graphs and form conclusions.

1 a A suitable plan could include the following: Measure out a set amount of water (e.g. 100 cm³) using an appropriately sized measuring cylinder. Heat the water to the desired temperature. Add the water to a beaker, cover the beaker with the first hat and start a stopwatch. Measure the temperature of the water under the hat every 2 minutes until 10 minutes has passed, using a datalogger with a temperature probe. Repeat the investigation with another hat using a new (unheated) beaker. A suitable diagram of apparatus included.

   b Same volume of water, water heated to same temperature before the investigation, beaker is sitting on same surface.

2 a If the beaker is not cooled down between investigations, the investigation will not be fair.

   b Safety glasses should be worn when heating the water. General care should be taken with regard to using uncluttered surroundings when carrying out investigations with hot water.

   c To check reliability of results.

3 a As the time increased, the average temperature of the water decreased (or the inverse – as the time decreased, the average temperature of the water increased). *Or* The longer the time, the cooler the average temperature of the water (or the inverse – the shorter the time, the hotter the average temperature of the water).

   b The one made of wool.

   c 50 °C

4 a As the temperature increased, the pressure inside the football increased (or the inverse – as the temperature decreased, the pressure inside the football decreased). *Or* The hotter the temperature, the higher the pressure (or the inverse – the colder the temperature, the lower the pressure).

   b As the temperature increased, the air particles in the football gained more and more energy and moved with increasing speed. When the particles collided with the wall of the football they exerted an increasingly large force.

   c 25 N/cm²

5 a Temperature probes connected to a datalogger.

   b

Material	Time taken to cause a 10 °C rise in the temperature of the end of the rod (seconds)
copper	35
iron	55
lead	130
steel	50

Extension – Plan and carry out an investigation to find out which pupil's coat sleeve is the best insulator of heat.

   Link – Exploring Science 8Id

Unit 8J MAGNETS AND ELECTROMAGNETS

The activities in this unit concern the variables affecting the strength of magnetic and electromagnetic fields. The activities can be used to help pupils identify variables, interpret tables and graphs, including deciding upon appropriate lines of best fit.

1 a B – held the most masses.

   b A – held the least masses.

   c Number of 1 g masses held before the basket fell.

   d The magnet.

2 a and b Any of the following variables could be changed: length of coil, number of turns on coil, material making up the core of the coil, current flowing through the coil. The mass that could be supported by the electromagnet when switched on could be the variable measured to determine the strength of the electromagnet. For example 'How does the strength of an electromagnet change with the number of turns in the coil?'

3 a **i** Number of coils on electromagnet. **ii** Mass of iron that could be supported by the electromagnet.

   b Best straight line.

   c One point (15 coils on the electromagnet) does not lie on the best straight line – it is an anomalous result.

4 a Unit for current is missing (amps).

   b As the current increases, the strength of the electromagnet increases (or the inverse – as the current decreases, the strength of the electromagnet decreases). *Or* The higher the current, the stronger the electromagnet (or the inverse – the lower the current, the weaker the electromagnet).

5 a

Material in the core of the electromagnet	Mass of iron which could be supported by electromagnet (g)
iron	10
copper	3
soft iron	14
steel	7

   b Soft iron.

Extension – Investigate as a class how a very strong electromagnet can be made.

Link – Exploring Science 8Jd

Unit 8K LIGHT

The activities in this unit concern the nature and properties of light. The activities can be used to help pupils identify variables, make predictions, select appropriate equipment, interpret tables and graphs and consider the validity of conclusions.

1

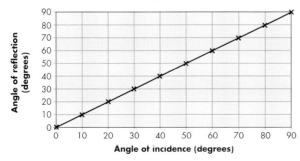

Effect of the angle of incidence of a ray of light on the angle of its reflection.

2 a Units missing (degrees or °).

   b The angle of incidence is always higher than the angle of refraction.

   c No. The range used was insufficient to be sure that the angle of refraction was always (and would always be) more than 5 degrees lower than the angle of incidence.

    d A variety of answers can be accepted, for example, difficulties in tracing rays of light due to ambient lighting or the divergence of a beam, limitations in the scales of protractors, equipment easily moved.

3 a **i** Distance over which light is visible. **ii** Brightness of light.

    b As the brightness of the light increases, the distance over which the light is visible increases (or the inverse – as the brightness of the light decreases, the distance over which the light is visible decreases). *Or* The brighter the light, the greater the distance over which it is visible (or the inverse – the dimmer the light, the lower the distance over which it is visible).

4 a

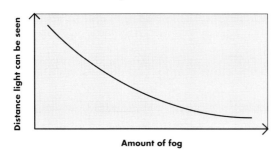

Effect of the amount of fog on the distance light can be seen.

(y-axis) Distance light can be seen

(x-axis) Amount of fog

    b Light meter (or light probe attached to datalogger).

5 a Only green light will be visible. When white light is viewed through a green filter only the green element of the light is able to travel through to the eye, the other colours are absorbed by the filter.

    b Black or no light. The green filter will have only let green light through, which would itself have been absorbed by the red filter. The absence of light is black.

Extension – Plan and carry out an investigation into the amounts of light that different materials will allow to pass through them. This gives opportunities for the use of ICT in the collection and presentation of data.

    Link – Exploring Science 8Kb

Unit 8L **SOUND AND HEARING**

The activities in this unit concern the nature of sound and an investigation into sound proofing. The activities can be used to help pupils identify variables, make predictions, frame questions, evaluate experimental procedures, interpret tables and graphs, including suggesting appropriate lines of best fit.

1 a How does the thickness of bubble wrap affect the volume of the ticking of the alarm clock?

    b A reasonable prediction would be 'As the thickness of the bubble wrap increases, the volume of the ticking of the alarm clock will decrease.' However, credit should be given for any prediction of a pattern between the variables.

    c A decibel meter.

2 a Method of measuring the volume of the ticking should be constant, distance from the clock to sound intensity measuring device (decibel meter) should be constant, noise from the outside environment should be constant. Type of bubble wrap used should be the same.

    b To check the reliability of data.

3 a The units of temperature and speed are missing.

    b Best curve.

    c As the temperature of the water increased, the speed of sound increased (or the inverse – as the temperature of the water decreased, the speed of sound decreased). *Or* The hotter the water, the faster the speed of sound (or the inverse – the colder the water the slower the speed of sound).

    d 1520 m/s (+/– 5 m/s).

4 a No. The older people could not hear sounds at the higher frequencies.

b For an investigation to be fair, all variables apart from that being investigated must be controlled. In this investigation the individuals involved would have varied in many different ways, for instance, the 25-year old may be suffering from an ear infection. Where humans are involved in investigations, the data gained can often only be used to make conclusions about the test subjects, not to form hypotheses about humans in general.

5 a How does the density of a substance affect the speed of sound through it?

b As the density of a substance increases, the speed of sound through it increases (or the inverse – as the density of a substance decreases, the speed of sound through it decreases). *Or* The denser the substance, the faster the speed of sound through it (or the inverse – the less dense the substance, the slower the speed of sound through it).

c 4500 m/s

Extension – Plan and carry out an investigation into the variables that affect the pitch of a note produced by blowing over a bottle or twanging a ruler.

Link – Exploring Science 8Lb

GRAPH QUESTIONS

Pupils could come up with a range of questions referring to any aspects of the graph on display. The examples below, whilst not exhaustive, act as a guide to the sorts of questions that pupils could suggest. See Skills progression chart on page vii for more information.

Variables:

Name the independent variable.

Name the dependent variable.

What is the question being investigated?

Say how you might have measured the independent and dependent variables.

Fair tests:

Which things would have been kept the same to make this a fair test?

Graph presentation:

Can you see any mistakes or omissions on this graph?

Graph interpretation:

What is the value of the dependent variable when the independent variable is ...? (Or the inverse.)

As the independent variable rises what happens to the dependent variable?

How does the independent variable affect the dependent variable? (Or the inverse.)

Can you see a pattern in these results?

At which point is the graph changing most rapidly? *Relating to the gradient of the graph.*

Graph prediction:

What do you think would happen to the shape of the graph if it were continued?

Anomalous results:

Which result(s) look anomalous?

What could have caused these anomalies?

What shape line of best fit would be used here?

Conclusions:

Explain why (state result/finding) has occurred.

Explain why this pattern has been found.

Evaluations:

How could the data on this graph be displayed in a better way? *By changing the type of graph, altering the axes, drawing a line of best fit.*

How could more information for this graph be obtained? *By altering the range/adding intermediate figures.*

TABLE QUESTIONS

Pupils could come up with a range of questions referring to any aspects of the table on display. The examples below, whilst not exhaustive, act as a guide to the sorts of questions that pupils could suggest. See Skills progression chart on page vii for more information.

Variables:

Name the independent variable.

Name the dependent variable.

What is the question being investigated?

Say how you might have measured the independent and dependent variables.

Fair test:

Which things would have been kept the same to make this a fair test?

Table presentation:

Can you see any mistakes or omissions on this table?

Can you suggest another way in which this data could be presented?

Table interpretation:

Which (state independent variable value) in the table has the largest/smallest (state dependent variable)?

How many times has this experiment been repeated?

Why has the experiment been repeated (insert number) times?

Are there any results on this table that look unlikely? Explain your answer to the above.

Conclusions:

What is the relationship between (state the independent variable) and (state the dependent variable)?

Can you see a pattern in these results?

Evaluations:

How could more information for this table be obtained? *By altering the range/adding intermediate figures, repeating the investigation (more times).*

STARTER WORKSHEET

1 What variables affect the size of potatoes?

Ravi wanted to find out what affected the size
of potatoes produced by a plant.

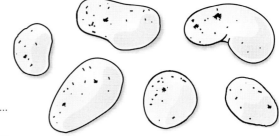

a Ravi could investigate many different
variables. Make a list of them.

....

....

....

b Write out a question which Ravi could investigate:

I am going to investigate how ....

....

c How could Ravi measure the size of the potatoes?

....

....

Link – Exploring Science 7Ab

Sc1 Skills for Key Stage 3 © Pearson Education Limited 2004

STARTER WORKSHEET

1 What variables affect the size of potatoes?

Ravi wanted to find out what affected the size
of potatoes produced by a plant.

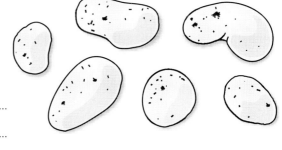

a Ravi could investigate many different
variables. Make a list of them.

....

....

....

b Write out a question which Ravi could investigate:

I am going to investigate how ....

....

c How could Ravi measure the size of the potatoes?

....

....

Link – Exploring Science 7Ab

Sc1 Skills for Key Stage 3 © Pearson Education Limited 2004

STARTER WORKSHEET

2 What variables affect the size of potatoes?

Ravi wanted to find out what affected the size of potatoes produced by a plant. He took three potato plants of the same species and planted all three in identical pots and soil in the school greenhouse. One plant was kept in full sunlight, the second was covered with a thin plastic bag which only let about half of the light through, the third was covered with a thick plastic bag which only let about a quarter of the light through.

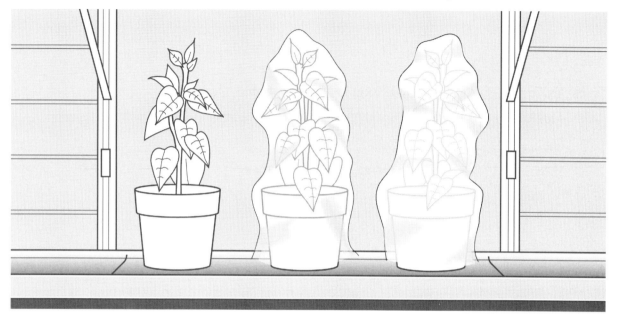

a What question was Ravi investigating?

....

....

b Which variables would Ravi have to keep the same to make the investigation fair?

....

....

c Sketch a graph predicting the outcome of this investigation.

d Explain why you have made this prediction.

....

....

....

Link – Exploring Science 7Ab

STARTER WORKSHEET

3   What variables affect the size of potatoes?

Ravi wanted to find out what affected the size of
potatoes produced by a plant. He took three potato
plants of the same species and planted all three in
the school greenhouse. One plant was kept in full
sunlight, the second was covered with a thin plastic
bag which only let about half of the light through,
the third was covered with a thick plastic bag which
only let about a quarter of the light through.

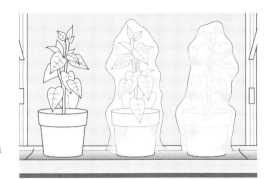

The results that Ravi obtained are shown in the table.

a   What information is missing from the table?

   ....

Intensity of sunlight	Average mass of potatoes
high	850
medium	440
low	320

b   Describe the pattern found in these results.

   ....

   ....

c   What type of graph would best present the data given in this table?

   ....

Link – Exploring Science 7Ab

Sc1 Skills for Key Stage 3 © Pearson Education Limited 2004

- ✂

STARTER WORKSHEET

1   Who is the fittest?

Steve and Derek wanted to find out
which of them was the fittest. They both
did some exercise which made them
breathe faster. They then stopped
exercising and timed how long it took for
their breathing rates to return to normal
again. The graph shows the results.

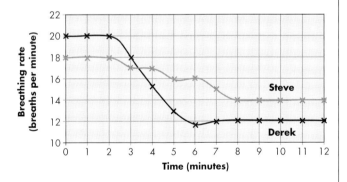

a   After how many minutes did
Steve and Derek stop exercising?   ....

Derek said that the faster a person's breathing rate returned to a steady resting rate,
the fitter the person was.

b   From the information in the graph, state who was the fittest person and explain why?

   ....

   ....

c   Suggest how this investigation may not have been fair.

   ....

   ....

Link – Exploring Science 9Ba

Sc1 Skills for Key Stage 3 © Pearson Education Limited 2004

STARTER WORKSHEET

2 Investigating smoking habits

An investigation was carried out into the effect of the number of cigarettes smoked per day on the number of people who died from lung cancer. The results are presented in the graph below.

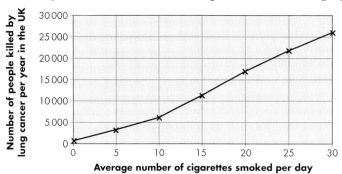

a Describe the pattern shown in the graph.

....

b Use your scientific knowledge to explain this pattern.

....

....

Link – Exploring Science 9Bb

Sc1 Skills for Key Stage 3 © Pearson Education Limited 2004

 ....

STARTER WORKSHEET

3 Does caffeine have an effect on reaction time?

Joanna investigated whether the amount of caffeine in her body affected her reaction time. Angela held a meter ruler above Joanna's hand and then let go without any warning. Joanna tried to react as quickly as she could by catching the ruler. The distance the ruler had fallen before Joanna reacted was then noted down in centimetres.

a Design a table to display this data.

35
no coffee
32 35

30   28
1 cup of coffee
32

18   15
3 cups of coffee
22

26   21
2 cups of coffee
22

b Add a column to the table and calculate the average for each amount of coffee.

c Describe the pattern you can see in these results. All the coffee that Joanna drank was of the same strength.

....

Link – Exploring Science 9Bd

Sc1 Skills for Key Stage 3 © Pearson Education Limited 2004

STARTER WORKSHEET

1 Investigating photosynthesis

Plants produce oxygen when they make food during the process of photosynthesis. Jean set up the investigation shown on the right.

She then pointed a spotlight at the apparatus from a distance of 10 cm and counted the number of bubbles of gas that were released in 2 minutes. She then moved the spotlight so that it was first 20 cm and then 30 cm away and counted the number of bubbles produced in 2 minutes for each distance.

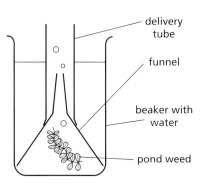

a What was the question that Jean was investigating?

....

b Predict the results of this investigation.

....

c Explain your reasons for your prediction in part (b).

....

....

Link – Exploring Science 9Ca

Sc1 Skills for Key Stage 3 © Pearson Education Limited 2004

✂

STARTER WORKSHEET

2 Investigating photosynthesis

Plants produce oxygen when they make food during the process of photosynthesis. Jean set up the investigation shown on the right.

She then pointed a spotlight the apparatus from a distance of 10 cm and counted the number of bubbles of gas that were released in 2 minutes. She then moved the spotlight so that it was first 20 cm and then 30 cm away and counted the number of bubbles produced in 2 minutes for each distance.

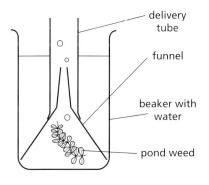

a What variables would Jean have to keep the same to make the investigation fair?

....

....

b Why is it important that Jean repeats her investigation?

....

c How many times should Jean repeat her investigation? ....

Link – Exploring Science 9Ca

Sc1 Skills for Key Stage 3 © Pearson Education Limited 2004

STARTER WORKSHEET

3 Investigating photosynthesis

Plants produce oxygen when they make food during the process of photosynthesis. Jean set up the investigation shown on the right.

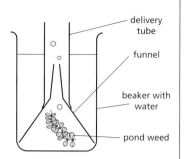

delivery tube

funnel

beaker with water

pond weed

She then pointed a spotlight at the apparatus from a distance of 10 cm and counted the number of bubbles of gas that were released in 2 minutes. She then moved the spotlight so that it was first 20 cm and then 30, 40 and 50 cm away and counted the number of bubbles produced in 2 minutes for each distance. The investigation was repeated three times at each distance.

Her results are shown on the right:

a Identify any results in the table that look unlikely.

....

b Explain you reason for your selection in part (a).

....

c If you had got these results, what would you do before calculating averages and plotting a graph?

....

Distance away from spotlight (cm)	Number of bubbles released in 2 minutes		
	Test 1	Test 2	Test 3
10	12	11	13
20	9	3	8
30	5	5	4
40	2	2	3
50	1	1	2

Link – Exploring Science 9Ca

Sc1 Skills for Key Stage 3 © Pearson Education Limited 2004

✄ ....

STARTER WORKSHEET

1 Interpreting graphs

Look at the graph on the right:

a What information is missing from the graph?

....

....

b What is the question that is being presented in this graph?

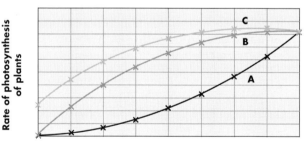

Rate of photosynthesis of plants

Light intensity

....

c Which of the three lines shown best represents your prediction of this relationship?

....

d Explain your choice of line.

....

....

Link – Exploring Science 9Dd

Sc1 Skills for Key Stage 3 © Pearson Education Limited 2004

STARTER WORKSHEET

2 Growing plants in greenhouses

The graph on the right shows the relationship between the temperature of a greenhouse and the amount of plant growth that occurs as a result.

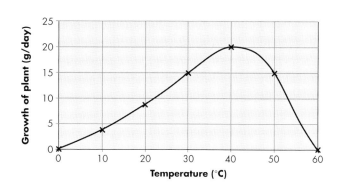

a Using the graph, describe how plant growth is affected by increasing temperature.

....

....

....

b Suggest a reason for the shape of the graph from 40 °C to 60 °C.

....

....

....

Link – Exploring Science 9Dd

Sc1 Skills for Key Stage 3 © Pearson Education Limited 2004

STARTER WORKSHEET

3 What happens to leaves in the dark?

The graph on the right shows the change in amount of starch remaining in a geranium leaf from the point where it was taken out of direct sunlight and placed in a darkened cupboard.

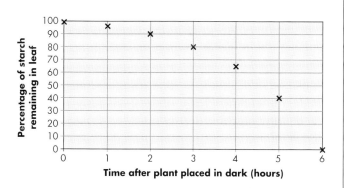

a What shape 'line of best fit' would you suggest for these points?

....

b Describe the pattern between time and amount of starch remaining in the leaf.

....

c Explain this pattern using your scientific knowledge and understanding.

....

....

....

Link – Exploring Science 9Da

Sc1 Skills for Key Stage 3 © Pearson Education Limited 2004

STARTER WORKSHEET

1 Metals and acids

When acids react with metals hydrogen gas is given off. The rate at which this gas is produced can be measured using the equipment shown below and timing how long it takes for the test tube to fill with hydrogen gas.

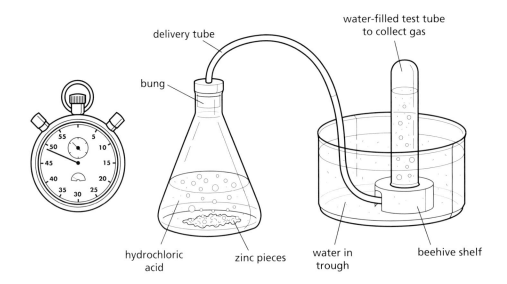

delivery tube

water-filled test tube to collect gas

bung

hydrochloric acid

zinc pieces

water in trough

beehive shelf

You have four pots containing filings of four different metals and five different concentrations of hydrochloric acid.

a Form a question for the investigation.

....

....

....

b What variables would you have to keep the same in your investigation?

....

....

....

c What safety procedures would you have to follow in your investigation?

....

....

....

....

Link – Exploring Science 9Eb

Sc1 Skills for Key Stage 3 © Pearson Education Limited 2004

STARTER WORKSHEET

2 Metals and acids

An investigation was carried out into the speed of production of hydrogen when different metals were combined with hydrochloric acid using the equipment shown below. The results that were obtained are shown in the table.

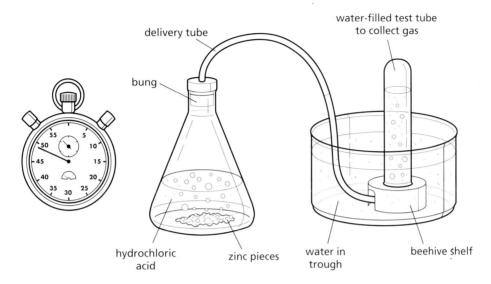

Metal	Time taken for the metal to release a test tube full of hydrogen (seconds)		
	Test 1	Test 2	Test 3
copper	75	85	83
zinc	26	30	72
iron	51	56	48
magnesium	10	12	11

a Name:

   i the independent variable

....

   ii the dependent variable.

....

b Identify any anomalous results from the table.

....

....

c If you had carried out this investigation, what would you do before calculating averages from the data?

....

....

....

d What type of graph would you use to represent this data?

....

Link – Exploring Science 9Eb

S T A R T E R   W O R K S H E E T

3 Metals and acids

Look at the graph:

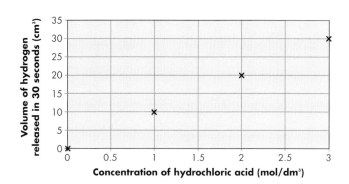

a Describe the pattern shown in this graph between the concentration of hydrochloric acid and the volume of hydrogen gas released in 30 seconds.

....

....

b Use the graph to predict the volume of hydrogen released in 30 seconds when the concentration of acid is:

i 1.5 mol/dm³ ....   **ii** 2.5 mol/dm³. ....

Link – Exploring Science 9Eb

Sc1 Skills for Key Stage 3 © Pearson Education Limited 2004

✂ ....

S T A R T E R   W O R K S H E E T

1 How quickly does magnesium react with acid?

You have been asked to investigate what affects how quickly magnesium metal reacts with acid.

a What variables could you investigate?

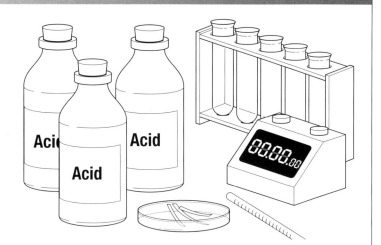

....

....

....

b Form a question for investigation.

....

....

c What variables would you have to keep the same to keep the investigation fair?

....

....

Link – Exploring Science 9Fb

Sc1 Skills for Key Stage 3 © Pearson Education Limited 2004

STARTER WORKSHEET

2 How quickly does magnesium react with acid?

Write out an investigative plan to find out how the concentration of acid affects the speed with which magnesium reacts using the following pieces of equipment:

Include details on:

a equipment used

b safety precautions

c how many times you would repeat the investigation and why.

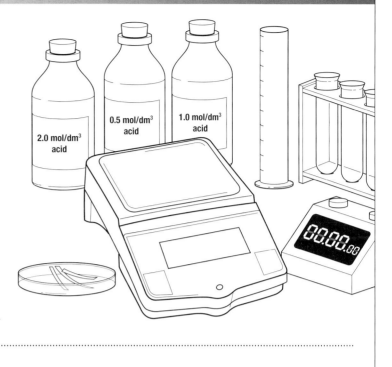

....

....

....

....

....

Link – Exploring Science 9Fb

Sc1 Skills for Key Stage 3 © Pearson Education Limited 2004

--✄

STARTER WORKSHEET

2 How quickly does magnesium react with acid?

Write out an investigative plan to find out how the concentration of acid affects the speed with which magnesium reacts using the following pieces of equipment:

Include details on:

a equipment used

b safety precautions

c how many times you would repeat the investigation and why.

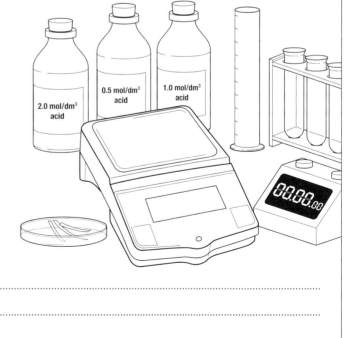

....

....

....

....

....

Link – Exploring Science 9Fb

Sc1 Skills for Key Stage 3 © Pearson Education Limited 2004 121

STARTER WORKSHEET

3 How quickly does magnesium react with acid?

An investigation was carried out to investigate how the concentration of acid affected the speed at which magnesium reacted.

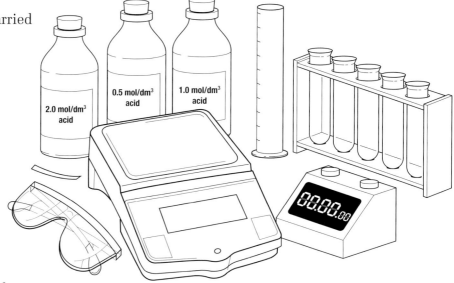

Look at the table of results.

Average time taken for 2 g of magnesium ribbon to go	Concentration of acid
1 min 13	0.5
47	1.0
31	1.5

a There are several things wrong with this table. What are they?

....

....

b Redraw the table correctly.

c Describe the pattern found in the results.

....

....

....

Link – Exploring Science 9Fb

STARTER WORKSHEET

1 How has global temperature changed?

Look at the graphs on the right:

a Describe what has happened to the temperature of the world since 1860.

....

....

....

....

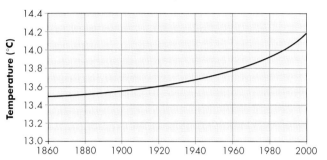

Change in global temperature 1860 – 2000.

b Suggest why this change has occurred.

....

....

....

....

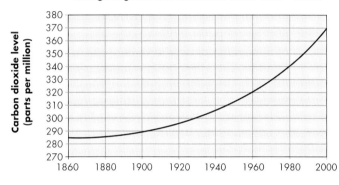

Change in global carbon dioxide levels 1860 – 2000.

Link – Exploring Science 9Gd

Sc1 Skills for Key Stage 3 © Pearson Education Limited 2004

✂

STARTER WORKSHEET

2 What happens to limestone over time?

An inscription was carved into a limestone plaque on an external wall to commemorate the building of a new community centre in 1980. The top picture shows what it looked like in 1980.

In 2000 the plaque looked like the bottom picture.

a What environmental process do you think could have caused this change in the inscription over the 20 years?

....

....

b Predict what you think the plaque would look like in 2020 if the same environmental conditions remained.

....

....

Link – Exploring Science 9Gb

Sc1 Skills for Key Stage 3 © Pearson Education Limited 2004

STARTER WORKSHEET

3 Investigating soil pH

Allan wanted to find out how the pH of soil affected the increase in mass of potatoes.

Here are his results:

pH of soil	Increase in mass of potatoes (g/day)
4.0	1.2
5.0	2.6
6.0	1.8
7.0	1.1

a Which soil pH produced the highest increase in the mass of the potatoes?

....

b Can you be sure of your answer to part (a)? What could you do to obtain more evidence for your conclusion?

....

....

Link – Exploring Science 9Ga

Sc1 Skills for Key Stage 3 © Pearson Education Limited 2004

✂ ....

STARTER WORKSHEET

1 Displacement reactions

When magnesium filings are added to copper sulphate, iron chloride and zinc chloride, a displacement reaction takes place which gives off heat. Corin wanted to find out which reaction gave off most heat.

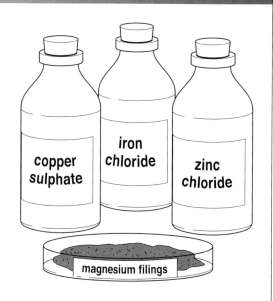

a Which pieces of equipment would allow Corin to best measure the temperature change in the reaction?

....

....

b What variables would Corin have to keep the same to make the investigation fair?

....

....

Link – Exploring Science 9Ha

Sc1 Skills for Key Stage 3 © Pearson Education Limited 2004

STARTER WORKSHEET

2 Displacement reactions

When magnesium filings are added to copper sulphate, iron chloride or zinc chloride, a displacement reaction takes place which gives off heat. Corin wanted to find out which reaction gave off most heat.

Corin carried out a trial of his investigation. He measured 50 cm³ of the solutions into a beaker and added 0.1 g of magnesium filings. The change in temperature of the solution was measured using a temperature probe and datalogger. The results he obtained are shown below:

Solution	Temperature change (°C)
copper sulphate	0.0
iron chloride	0.0
zinc chloride	0.1

a What changes could you suggest to Corin's plan to make the results clearer?

....

....

....

....

b How many times should Corin repeat his readings? ....

c Explain your answer to part (b).

....

....

....

....

....

Link – Exploring Science 9Ha

STARTER WORKSHEET

3 Displacement reactions

When magnesium filings are added to copper sulphate, iron chloride and zinc chloride, a displacement reaction takes place which gives off heat. Corin wanted to find out which reaction gave off most heat.

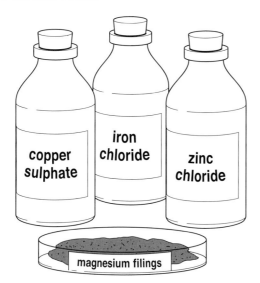

The results he obtained are shown below:

Solution	Temperature change (°C)		
	Test 1	Test 2	Test 3
copper sulphate	4.5	4.1	4.3
iron chloride	13.0	8.2	7.9
zinc chloride	22.1	20.8	22.8

a Identify the result from the table that seems unlikely.

....

b Suggest a reason that could explain this anomalous result.

....

....

....

....

c If these were your results, what steps would you take before calculating averages?

....

....

....

....

....

d What type of graph would best present these results?

....

Link – Exploring Science 9Ha

Sc1 Skills for Key Stage 3 © Pearson Education Limited 2004

STARTER WORKSHEET

1 Is there a link between voltage and resistance?

Darmesh investigated how the voltage of a power pack affected the amount of energy that was transferred to a resistor.

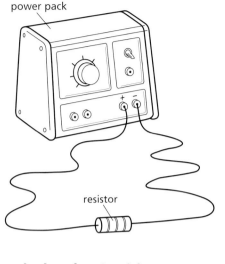

power pack

a Name:

   i the independent variable

   ....

   ii the dependent variable.

   ....

b What piece of equipment would best measure the energy transferred to the resistor?

....

c How would the piece of equipment selected for (b) be attached to the circuit?

....

....

resistor

Link – Exploring Science 9Ib

Sc1 Skills for Key Stage 3 © Pearson Education Limited 2004

STARTER WORKSHEET

2 Is there a link between voltage and resistance?

Darmesh investigated how the voltage of a power pack affected the amount of energy that was transferred to a resistor. The power pack supplied up to 12 V, although the resistor was only designed for use up to 6 V.

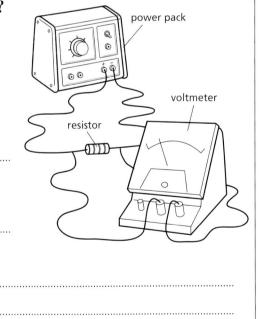

power pack

voltmeter

resistor

a Suggest a suitable range of power pack voltages for this investigation.

....

b How many times would you repeat this investigation?

....

c Explain your answer to part (c).

....

....

....

Link – Exploring Science 9Ib

Sc1 Skills for Key Stage 3 © Pearson Education Limited 2004

STARTER WORKSHEET

3 Is there a link between voltage and resistance?

Darmesh investigated how the voltage of a power pack affected the amount of energy that was transferred to a resistor. Here are his results plotted on a graph:

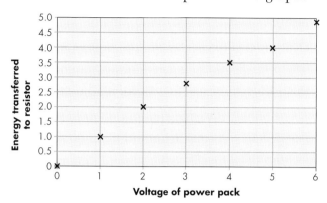

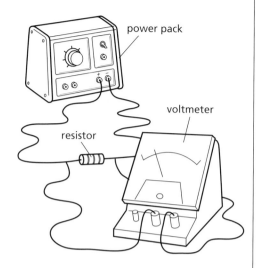

a What information is missing from the graph? ....

b Describe the pattern shown in these results.

....

c Which type of 'line of best fit' would you use to show this pattern? ....

Link – Exploring Science 9Ib

Sc1 Skills for Key Stage 3 © Pearson Education Limited 2004

✂ ···

STARTER WORKSHEET

1 Comparing mass and gravity

Look at the information in the table:

Planet	Mass of planet (Earth = 1)	Surface gravity (N/kg)
Mercury	0.1	3.6
Venus	0.8	8.6
Earth	1.0	9.8
Mars	0.1	3.7
Jupiter	318	25.9
Saturn	95	

a Which planet has the highest surface gravity?

....

b Describe the pattern between the mass of the planet and the surface gravity.

....

....

c Predict the value of surface gravity for Saturn. Explain why you have predicted this value.

....

....

Link – Exploring Science 9Jb

128

Sc1 Skills for Key Stage 3 © Pearson Education Limited 2004

STARTER WORKSHEET

2 Comparing speed and distance from Earth

Many satellites orbit the Earth. The speed at which they move depends upon their distance from the Earth.

Look at the information in the table:

a Describe the pattern that you can see between the distance from the Earth and the speed of the satellites.

....

....

....

Distance from Earth (km)	speed (km/s)
1 000	9.2
4 000	4.5
7 000	2.1
10 000	1.7

b The European Space Agency put two new satellites into orbit around the Earth. A monitoring satellite called MapSat was given an orbit of 2000 km whilst a telecommunications satellite called TelSat was placed at 12 000 km. Predict the speeds of the two satellites.

i MapSat = ...   **ii** TelSat = ...

Link – Exploring Science 9Jd

STARTER WORKSHEET

3 The force of gravity

The force of gravity between two masses is affected by two variables:

1 It increases as the size of the masses increases.

2 It decreases as the distance between the masses increases.

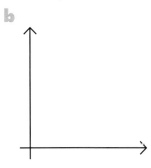

Sketch two graphs to show these relationships:

a

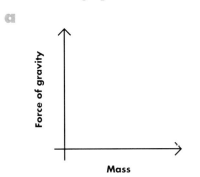

b

Link – Exploring Science 9Jb

129

STARTER WORKSHEET

1 Which shapes are most streamlined?

Katie wanted to find out which shape of plasticine was the most streamlined. She was given the following pieces of equipment:

a Plan how Katie could use these pieces of equipment to investigate how the shape of a piece of plasticine affected the time it took to fall through some wallpaper paste.

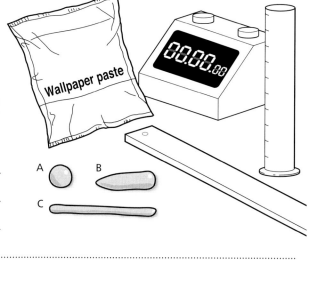

....

....

....

....

....

b List the variables that Katie would have to keep the same to make the investigation fair.

....

....

Link – Exploring Science 9Kc

Sc1 Skills for Key Stage 3 © Pearson Education Limited 2004

 ··

STARTER WORKSHEET

1 Which shapes are most streamlined?

Katie wanted to find out which shape of plasticine was the most streamlined. She was given the following pieces of equipment:

a Plan how Katie could use these pieces of equipment to investigate how the shape of a piece of plasticine affected the time it took to fall through some wallpaper paste.

....

....

....

....

b List the variables that Katie would have to keep the same to make the investigation fair.

....

....

Link – Exploring Science 9Kc

Sc1 Skills for Key Stage 3 © Pearson Education Limited 2004

STARTER WORKSHEET

2 Which shapes are most streamlined?

Katie investigated which shape of plasticine was the most streamlined.

Her results are shown below:

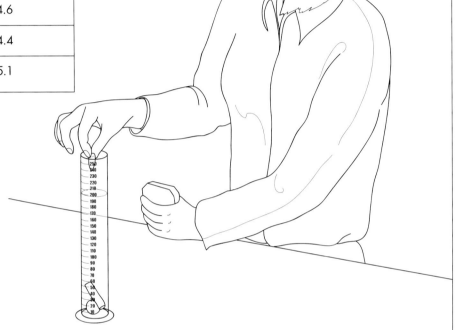

Shape	Time taken to fall through wallpaper paste
⬭	4.6
⬭	4.4
⬭	5.1

a What information is missing from the table?

....

....

b Which was the most streamlined piece of plasticine?

....

c How sure can you be of your answer to part (b)?
What could you do to gain more evidence for this conclusion?

....

....

....

....

....

....

Link – Exploring Science 9Kc

STARTER WORKSHEET

3 Which shape is most streamlined?

Katie investigated which shape of plasticine was most streamlined. She set up the investigation shown below and dropped in three different shaped pieces of plasticine. Katie timed how long each piece took from when it hit the top of the paste to when it stopped moving at the bottom.

a How fair do you think Katie's investigation was? Note down any problems you think she may have had.

....

....

....

b If you were to repeat this investigation, how would you make sure that it was fair?

....

....

....

Link – Exploring Science 9Kc

Sc1 Skills for Key Stage 3 © Pearson Education Limited 2004

- -

STARTER WORKSHEET

1 How does depth affect water pressure?

Look at the graph showing the changes in water pressure with depth:

a Describe the pattern shown in the graph.

....

....

....

b Predict what would happen to the size of an inflated balloon if it was carried down beneath the surface of the water by a diver.

....

....

c Explain your reasons for your prediction in part (b).

....

....

Link – Exploring Science 9Lb

Sc1 Skills for Key Stage 3 © Pearson Education Limited 2004

STARTER WORKSHEET

2 How are area and pressure linked?

Your teacher has asked you to investigate
the effect of the area of a dish on the
pressure it produces when holding a
1 kg mass. You have been given a
range of different sized dishes, a
1 kg mass and a tray filled with a
layer of plasticine.

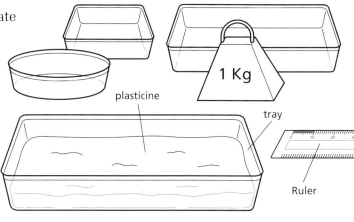

plasticine

tray

Ruler

a Predict a pattern between the
area of the dishes and the
pressure produced by the 1 kg
mass.

....

....

b Explain the reasons for your prediction.

....

....

Link – Exploring Science 9Lb

✂

STARTER WORKSHEET

3 How are area and pressure linked?

Sarah investigated the effect of the area of a dish on the
pressure it produced when holding a 1 kg mass. She placed
a 1 kg mass on a dish which was then placed on a tray
filled with plasticine. After 1 minute, Sarah measured the
depth of the imprint made by the dish in the plasticine.

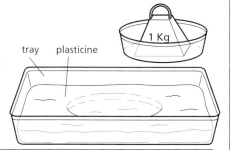

tray   plasticine

Sarah's results are shown in the table.

a Describe the pattern found in these results.

Area of dish (cm²)	Depth of imprint (mm)
10	5
15	3
25	2

....

....

b Predict the depth of imprint that would be made by a dish with an area of 8 cm².

....

c Predict the area of a dish which caused a 3.5 mm imprint. ....

d What could you do with the results in this table that would make predictions easier to
make and more accurate?

....

Link – Exploring Science 9Lb

STARTER THINKING SKILLS

Concentration of sugar (mg/ cm³)	Length of pollen tube after 1 hour (mm)			
	Test 1	Test 2	Test 3	Test 4
0.1	1.2	1.1	1.3	1.0
0.2	2.3	2.6	2.5	2.4
0.3	4.8	5.1	4.9	4.8
0.4	1.9	1.8	3.1	1.7
0.5	0.8	0.6	0.5	0.6

Look at the table. What does it tell us?

....

....

Tables present data and help us to answer questions and see patterns in results. What questions could you ask about this table that other people in your class could answer?

....

....

....

....

Sc1 Skills for Key Stage 3 © Pearson Education Limited 2004

✂ ....

STARTER THINKING SKILLS

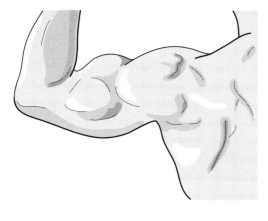

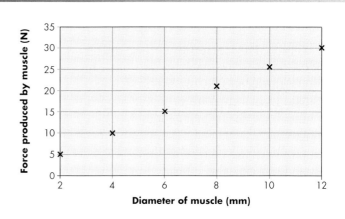

Look at the graph. What does it tell us?

....

Graphs help us to answer questions and see patterns in results. What questions could you ask about this graph that other people in your class could answer?

....

....

....

Sc1 Skills for Key Stage 3 © Pearson Education Limited 2004

STARTER **THINKING SKILLS**

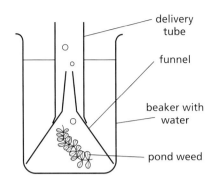

delivery tube

funnel

beaker with water

pond weed

The effect of light intensity on gas production of pond weed.

Look at the graph. What does it tell us?

....

Graphs help us to answer questions and see patterns in results. What questions could you ask about this graph that other people in your class could answer?

....

....

....

STARTER **THINKING SKILLS**

Amount of fertiliser (g/dm³ of water)	Growth of plant stem (mm/day)		
	Test 1	Test 2	Test 3
1	1.8	1.6	2.1
2	3.8	3.5	3.8
3	6.7	7.2	6.5
4	9.5	10.1	9.8
5	11.2	18.9	11.1

FERTILISER

Look at the table. What does it tell us?

....

Tables present data and help us to answer questions and see patterns in results. What questions could you ask about this table that other people in your class could answer?

....

....

....

....

STARTER THINKING SKILLS

Look at the graph. What does it tell us?

....

....

....

....

....

....

Effect of acid concentration on heat released when reacted with magnesium.

Graphs help us to answer questions and see patterns in results. What questions could you ask about this graph that other people in your class could answer?

....

....

....

....

....

Sc1 Skills for Key Stage 3 © Pearson Education Limited 2004

STARTER THINKING SKILLS

Look at the graph. What does it tell us?

....

....

....

....

....

....

Effect of time on the mass of calcium carbonate when added to acid.

Graphs help us to answer questions and see patterns in results. What questions could you ask about this graph that other people in your class could answer?

....

....

....

....

....

Sc1 Skills for Key Stage 3 © Pearson Education Limited 2004

STARTER **THINKING SKILLS**

Mass of lime added to soil (g/dm³ of soil)	pH of soil				
	Test 1	Test 2	Test 3	Test 4	Test 5
0	4.5	4.5	4.5	4.6	4.4
1	4.9	4.8	4.9	4.8	4.8
2	5.2	5.2	5.3	5.4	5.2
3	5.6	4.5	5.6	5.8	5.7
5	6.3	6.1	6.2	6.0	6.3
7	6.8	6.7	6.7	6.7	6.7

Look at the table. What does it tell us?

....

Tables present data and help us to answer questions and see patterns in results. What questions could you ask about this table that other people in your class could answer?

....

....

Sc1 Skills for Key Stage 3 © Pearson Education Limited 2004

STARTER **THINKING SKILLS**

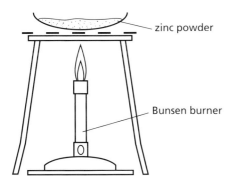

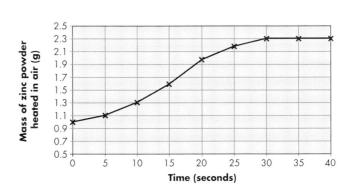

Look at the graph. What does it tell us?

....

Graphs help us to answer questions and see patterns in results. What questions could you ask about this graph that other people in your class could answer?

....

....

....

....

Sc1 Skills for Key Stage 3 © Pearson Education Limited 2004

STARTER THINKING SKILLS

1.5 V battery

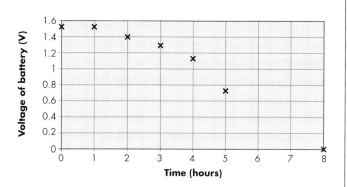

Look at the graph. What does it tell us?

....

Graphs help us to answer questions and see patterns in results. What questions could you ask
about this graph that other people in your class could answer?

....

....

....

....

Sc1 Skills for Key Stage 3 © Pearson Education Limited 2004

STARTER THINKING SKILLS

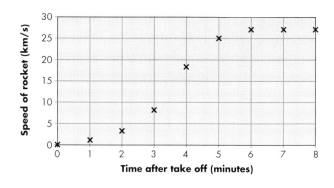

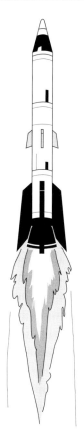

Look at the graph. What does it tell us?

....

Graphs help us to answer questions and see patterns in results. What questions
could you ask about this graph that other people in your class could answer?

....

....

....

....

Sc1 Skills for Key Stage 3 © Pearson Education Limited 2004

STARTER **THINKING SKILLS**

Mass (kg)	Acceleration of object when a force of 10 N is applied (m/s^2)
1	10.0
2	5.0
3	3.3
4	2.5
5	2.0

Look at the table. What does it tell us?

....

Tables present data and help us to answer questions and see patterns in results. What questions could you ask about this table that other people in your class could answer?

....

....

....

....

Sc1 Skills for Key Stage 3 © Pearson Education Limited 2004

STARTER **THINKING SKILLS**

Mass of air in tyres (kg)	Air Pressure in tyres (N/m^2)
0.5	20
1.0	40
1.5	60
2.0	81
2.5	104

Look at the table. What does it tell us?

....

Tables present data and help us to answer questions and see patterns in results. What questions could you ask about this table that other people in your class could answer?

....

....

....

....

Sc1 Skills for Key Stage 3 © Pearson Education Limited 2004

Unit 9A **INHERITANCE AND SELECTION**

The activities in this unit concern an investigation into the effect of the environment on the growth of potatoes. The activities can be used to help pupils identify variables, plan fair tests, make predictions, interpret information in tables and select appropriate graphs.

1 a Intensity of light, amount of water, amount of minerals in the soil, temperature and humidity of the environment potatoes grown in, time potatoes left to grow.

   b How does the intensity of light (for example) affect the average mass of potatoes produced by a plant?

   c Find the mass of the potatoes using an electronic balance (and calculate the average mass of the potatoes).

2 a How does the intensity of light affect the average mass of potatoes produced by a plant?

   b Amount of water, amount of minerals in the soil, temperature and humidity of the environment potatoes grown in, time potatoes left to grow.

   c The graph should show that when the intensity of light increases, the average mass of the potatoes will increase (however, give credit where an alternative prediction is backed up by a valid reason in part d).

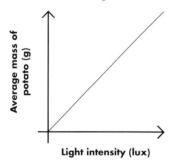

Light intensity (lux)

   d Discuss pupils' reasons. A good explanation might be 'The more light a plant gets, the more it can photosynthesise and so the more food it can make to send to the potatoes for storage'.

3 a The units (g) from the second column of the table.

   b As the intensity of light increased, the average size of the potatoes increased (or the inverse – as the intensity of light decreased, the average size of the potatoes decreased).
      Or The brighter the light (the stronger the light intensity), the larger the average size of the potatoes (or the inverse – the dimmer the light (the weaker the light intensity), the smaller the average size of the potatoes).

   c A bar graph.

Extension – Plan and carry out an investigation into the growth of plants in different environmental conditions – consider using fast-cycling brassicae as the experimental plant.

Unit 9B **FIT AND HEALTHY**

The activities in this unit concern the interpretation and presentation of data regarding health-related topics. The activities can be used to help pupils design and interpret tables, interpret graphs, describe and explain patterns in data and evaluate the validity of conclusions.

1 a 2 minutes

   b Derek – as his breathing rate returned to a steady resting rate before Steve.

   c Derek and Steve may have been exercising to varying degrees, accounting for the fact that Steve took longer to recover.

2 a As the average number of cigarettes smoked per day increases, the number of people dying from lung cancer increases (or the inverse – as the average number of cigarettes smoked per day decreases, the number of people dying from lung cancer decreases). *Or* The greater the average number of cigarettes smoked per day, the greater the number of people dying from lung cancer (or the inverse – the smaller the average number of cigarettes smoked per day, the smaller the number of people dying from lung cancer).

   b The more cigarettes smoked per day, the more carcinogenic tar is deposited in the lungs, increasing the likelihood of the emergence of cancer.

3   a and b

Number of cups of coffee	Distance ruler fell before being caught (cm)			
	Test 1	Test 2	Test 3	Average
0	35	32	35	34
1	30	28	32	30
2	26	21	22	23
3	18	15	24	19

   c   As the number of cups of coffee increased, the distance the ruler fell before being caught decreased (or the inverse – as the number of cups of coffee decreased, the distance the ruler fell before being caught increased). *Or* The more coffee drunk, the less distance the ruler fell (or the inverse – the less coffee drunk, the greater distance the ruler fell).

Extension – Plan and carry out an investigation into the response of the heart rate to exercise.

     Link – Exploring Science 9Ba

Unit 9C   PLANTS AND PHOTOSYNTHESIS

The activities in this unit concern an investigation into the rate of oxygen production in pond weed. The activities can be used to help pupils form questions, plan fair tests and identify and respond to anomalous results presented in tables.

1   a   How does the intensity of light affect the number of bubbles produced (or the amount of photosynthesis)?

   b   A good prediction would be 'As the intensity of light increases, the number of bubbles will increase'. However, credit should be given for variations so long as they are backed up with reasoned explanations in part (c).

   c   More light will give the plant more energy, allowing it to photosynthesise more quickly and to make more oxygen.

2   a   Temperature, pH of water, CO_2 concentration in water.

   b   To ensure reliability of data and to identify any anomalous results.

   c   A minimum of five times.

3   a   20 cm distance, Test 2.

   b   This figure is very different from those gained from the first and third tests at this distance suggesting that the result is anomalous.

   c   Repeat the reading for the anomalous result and use this new data for the calculation of averages.

Extension – Plan and carry out an investigation into how the amount of carbon dioxide in the water affects the rate of oxygen production in pond weed.

     Link – Exploring Science 9Ca.

   Challenge more able pupils to investigate two variables rather than just carbon dioxide levels.

Unit 9D   PLANTS FOR FOOD

The activities in this unit concern some interpretive exercises based around the topic of photosynthesis. The activities can be used to help pupils produce and interpret graphs, including drawing lines of best fit and forming explanations based on scientific knowledge and understanding.

1   a   units

   b   How does the intensity of light affect the rate of photosynthesis of plants?

   c   Line B.

   d   Line A is incorrect as it suggests that the more light available, the faster photosynthesis occurs. In fact at certain light intensities chloroplasts are damaged and other factors begin to limit the rate of photosynthesis. Line C is incorrect as it suggests that plants can photosynthesise when there is no light. Line B is correct as it shows that the rate of photosynthesis levels off as other factors such as carbon dioxide concentration, temperature and water availability begin to limit the process.

2 a As temperature increases from 0 to 40 °C, the amount of plant growth increases. However, from 40 to 60 °C the amount of plant growth decreases to zero.

   b Above 40 °C some of the enzymes carrying out the process of photosynthesis and respiration begin to denature (break down), causing growth to stop.

3 a Best curve.

   b As the time after being placed in the darkness increases, the amount of starch remaining in the leaf decreases.

   c The leaf is in darkness and so cannot photosynthesise and produce more starch. The starch that was present at the start of the investigation is converted into glucose. This is then used by the leaf in the process of respiration.

Extension – Plan and carry out an investigation into the effects of fertilisers on the growth of duckweed. Present data in tables and graphs.

   Link – Exploring Science 9Db

Unit 9E   REACTIONS OF METALS AND METAL COMPOUNDS

The activities in this unit are based around an investigation into the reactions of metals and acid. The activities can be used to help pupils form questions for investigation, plan fair tests, identify anomalous results in tables, and interpret and make predictions from graphs.

1 a How does the type of metal affect the time taken for a test tube of hydrogen to be produced (the rate of hydrogen production)? *Or* How does the concentration of acid affect the time taken for a test tube of hydrogen to be produced (the rate of hydrogen production)?

   b Either question will need these variables controlled – the temperature of the acid, the size of the test tube used, the amount of acid used, the amount of metal used. Where the type of metal is the independent variable the concentration of acid will also need to be controlled. Where the concentration of acid is the independent variable the type of metal will need to be controlled.

   c Standard safety procedures associated with the use of acids, e.g. safety glasses, hazard cards available, procedures for dealing with spillages.

2 a **i** Type of metal. **ii** Time taken for metal to release a test tube full of hydrogen (seconds).

   b Zinc – Test 3.

   c Repeat the investigation for zinc and use this figure instead of the anomalous one when calculating averages.

   d A bar graph.

3 a As the concentration of acid increases, the volume of hydrogen gas released in 30 seconds increases (or the inverse – as the concentration of acid decreases, the volume of hydrogen gas released in 30 seconds decreases). *Or* The higher the concentration of acid, the greater the volume of hydrogen released in 30 seconds (or the inverse – the lower the concentration of acid, the lower the volume of hydrogen released in 30 seconds).

   b **i** 15 cm^3 **ii** 25 cm^3

Extension – Plan an investigation into the effects of temperature of acid on the rate of hydrogen production when a metal is added.

   Link – Exploring Science 9Eb

Unit 9F   PATTERNS OF REACTIVITY

The activities in this unit are based around an investigation into the speed of reaction of magnesium and acid. The activities can be used to help pupils form questions for investigation, plan fair tests, construct tables and describe patterns between variables.

1 a Concentration of acid, amount of magnesium, temperature of acid.

   b How does … (any of the variables above) … affect how quickly magnesium reacts with acid?

   c Variables to be kept the same (controlled) would be those two variables named in part (a) that have not been selected as the independent variable.

Sc1 Skills for Key Stage 3 © Pearson Education Limited 2004

2 **a, b** and **c** For example: Measure out 20 cm³ of 0.5 mol/dm³ acid into a test tube using a 50 cm³ measuring cylinder (wear safety glasses). Weigh out 2 g of magnesium ribbon using an electronic balance. Place the magnesium ribbon in the test tube of acid and start timing with an electronic stopwatch. Stop timing when all of the magnesium has reacted and disappeared from sight. Repeat the investigation with 1.0 and 1.5 mol/dm³ acid. Repeat the whole investigation five times to check results for reliability.

3 **a** No units in table headings (seconds (or s) for time and mol/dm³ for acid concentration), independent and dependent variables in the wrong columns, unclear heading for dependent variable, 'Average time taken for 2 g of magnesium ribbon to go', inconsistent units in results (use of minutes as well as seconds).

b

Concentration of acid (mol/dm³)	Average time taken for 2 g of magnesium ribbon to fully react with the acid (seconds)
0.5	73
1.0	47
1.5	31

c As the concentration of the acid increases, the time taken for the magnesium ribbon to fully react with the acid decreases (or the inverse – as the concentration of the acid decreases, the time taken for the magnesium ribbon to fully react with the acid increases). *Or* The stronger the acid, the quicker the magnesium ribbon reacts (or the inverse – the weaker the acid, the slower the magnesium ribbon reacts).

Extension – Plan and carry out an investigation into how the volume of acid affects the rate of reaction with magnesium ribbon.

Link – Exploring Science 9Fd

Unit 9G ENVIRONMENTAL CHEMISTRY

The activities in this unit are based around the effects of the chemical environment. The activities can be used to help pupils interpret observations, tables and graphs.

1 **a** The temperature of the world has increased (give extra credit if pupils give a figure, i.e. 'by 0.7 °C')

b Reference should be made to the second graph with the suggestion that the rise in global temperature is caused by a parallel increase in carbon dioxide concentration.

2 **a** Chemical weathering by acid rain.

b The inscription would be even less distinct.

3 **a** pH 5.0

b Repeat the investigation but alter the range to include intermediate pH values.

Extension – Examine data on global climate change and make predictions for the future of the planet.

Link – Exploring Science 9Gd

Unit 9H USING CHEMISTRY

The activities in this unit concern an investigation into the exothermic nature of displacement reactions. The activities can be used to help pupils to plan fair investigations with appropriate selection of equipment, values of variables (based upon trials) and repetitions, identify anomalous results from tables and select suitable graphs.

1 **a** Temperature probe with datalogger.

b Mass of magnesium, volume of metal in solution, starting temperature of solution.

2 **a** Either increase the mass of magnesium or reduce the volume of solution used.

b At least five times.

c So that results can be checked against each other to ensure reliability of data.

3 **a** Iron chloride – Test 1.

b Incorrect measurement of magnesium or the metal solution, faulty datalogger or poorly calibrated probe.

   c   Repeat the reading for iron chloride.

   d   A bar graph.

Extension – Plan and carry out an investigation into the exothermic nature of displacement reactions using datalogging equipment – present data using computer generated graphs.

   Link – Exploring Science 9Ha

Unit 9I ENERGY AND ELECTRICITY

The activities in this unit are based around an investigation into the energy transferred to a resistor in a simple series circuit. The activities can be used to help pupils to form questions for investigation, plan fair tests with appropriate selection of equipment, ranges and repetitions, describe patterns in results and select appropriate lines of best fit.

1 a **i** Voltage of the power pack. **ii** Amount of energy transferred to the resistor.

   b A (digital) voltmeter.

   c In parallel.

2 a e.g. 1, 2, 3, 4, 5, 6 (or 0.5 V steps).

   b Five times.

   c To check the reliability of the results.

3 a The units on the axes, title, line of best fit.

   b As the voltage of the power pack increases, the amount of energy transferred to the resistor increases (or the inverse – as the voltage of the power pack decreases, the amount of energy transferred to the resistor decreases). *Or* The higher the voltage on the power pack, the higher the amount of energy transferred to the resistor (or the inverse – the lower the voltage on the power pack, the lower the amount of energy transferred to the resistor).

   c Best curve.

Extension – Plan and carry out an investigation into the effect of power pack voltage on current through a series circuit. Challenge pupils to explain why there is a directly proportional relationship.

Unit 9J GRAVITY AND SPACE

The activities in this unit are based around interpretations of tables and graphs of planetary data. The activities can be used to help pupils to interpret tables, describe relationships between variables and present these graphically.

1 a Jupiter

   b As the mass of the planet increases, the surface gravity of the planet increases (or the inverse – as the mass of the planet decreases, the surface gravity of the planet decreases). *Or* The bigger the mass of the planet, the greater the surface gravity (or the inverse – the smaller the mass of the planet, the less the surface gravity).

   c Any figure between 9.8 and 25.9 (the correct figure is 11). The explanation for this prediction should be based upon the pattern that is evident from the table.

2 a As the distance from the Earth increases, the speed of the satellite decreases (or the inverse – as the distance from the Earth decreases, the speed of the satellite increases). *Or* The greater the distance from the Earth, the slower the satellite moves (or the inverse – the lower the distance from the Earth, the faster the satellite moves).

   b **i** Any figure between 4.6 and 9.1 km/s. **ii** Below 1.7 km/s.

3 a Graph showing that an increase of mass leads to an increase in the force of gravity.

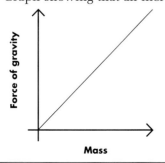

Sc1 Skills for Key Stage 3 © Pearson Education Limited 2004

b Graph showing that an increase in separation of the masses leads to a decrease in the force of gravity.

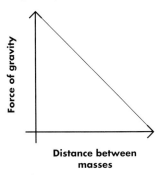

Distance between masses

Extension – Challenge pupils to represent a range of patterns in graphical form. For example, between the speed of satellites and their height of orbit, between the time taken for some planets to orbit the Sun and their distance from the Sun.

Unit 9K **SPEEDING UP**

The activities in this unit are based around an investigation into streamlining. The activities can be used to plan fair tests, interpret results in tables, and evaluate experimental procedures and the reliability of conclusions.

1 a For example: Fill a measuring cylinder with 200 cm³ of wallpaper paste. Mark the cylinder with a start (on 150 cm³ line) and end (on 50 cm³ line) point for timing. Drop the shape into the cylinder. Start the stopwatch when the shape passes the start point. Stop the stopwatch when the shape passes the end point. Repeat the experiment with other shapes.

b Mass of plasticine used for shapes, batch of wallpaper paste, method of timing, distance for mass to fall.

2 a Units of time.

b The bullet-shaped piece.

c One set of results is insufficient to be sure that the bullet-shaped piece of plasticine is the most streamlined. The investigation would need to be repeated a minimum of five times to check the reliability of the data.

3 a Difficulties with timing as the stopwatch has to be started just after the shape is dropped. Distance the shapes fall alters as shapes build up at the bottom of the cylinder.

b Mark the start point a few cm below the top surface to give time to start the stopwatch accurately. Mark the end point a few cm up from the bottom of the cylinder, leaving space for used plasticine shapes to collect. Alternatively, one person could act as a timer and a second person as a dropper.

Extension – Ask pupils to swap books and evaluate each others investigations, focusing on plans or conclusions.

Unit 9L **PRESSURE AND MOMENTS**

The activities in this unit are based around investigations into pressure. The activities can be used to practise making predictions based on prior knowledge, and from tables and graphs, describing patterns between variables and forming reasoned conclusions.

1 a As the depth increases the water pressure increases (or the inverse – as the depth decreases the water pressure decreases). *Or* The deeper the depth, the higher the water pressure (or the inverse – the shallower the depth, the lower the water pressure).

b The inflated balloon would decrease in size the deeper it got.

c The increasing water pressure would exert a force on the sides of the balloon, compressing the gas contained inside.

2 a As the area of the dishes increases, the depth of the imprint will decrease (or the inverse – as the area of the dishes decreases, the depth of the imprint will increase).

b The larger the area of the dish, the more spread out the force of the mass becomes / the lower the pressure caused by the mass on the tray.

3 a As the area of the dishes increases, the depth of the imprint decreases.

   b Greater than 5 mm.

   c Between 15.1 and 9.9 mm.

   d Plot a line graph so that the graph can be used for interpolation / extrapolation of results.

Extension – Pupils should make predictions / interpolations from a range of line graphs.

GRAPH QUESTIONS

Pupils could come up with a range of questions referring to any aspects of the graph on display. The examples below, whilst not exhaustive, act as a guide to the sorts of questions that pupils could suggest. See Skills progression chart on page vii for more information.

Variables:

Name the independent variable.

Name the dependent variable.

What is the question being investigated?

Say how you might have measured the independent and dependent variables.

Fair tests:

Which things would have been kept the same to make this a fair test?

Graph presentation:

Can you see any mistakes or omissions on this graph?

Graph interpretation:

What is the value of the dependent variable when the independent variable is ...? (Or the inverse.)

As the independent variable rises, what happens to the dependent variable?

How does the independent variable affect the dependent variable? (Or the inverse.)

Can you see a pattern in these results?

At which point is the graph changing most rapidly? *Relating to the gradient of the graph.*

Graph prediction:

What do you think would happen to the shape of the graph if it were continued?

Anomalous results:

Which result(s) look anomalous?

What could have caused these anomalies?

What shape line of best fit would be used here?

Conclusions:

Explain why (state result or finding) has occurred.

Explain why this pattern has been found.

Evaluations:

How could the data on this graph be displayed in a better way? *By changing the type of graph, altering the axes, drawing a line of best fit.*

How could more information for this graph be obtained? *By altering the range/adding intermediate figures.*

TABLE QUESTIONS

Pupils could come up with a range of questions referring to any aspects of the table on display. The examples below, whilst not exhaustive, act as a guide to the sorts of questions that pupils could suggest. See Skills progression chart on page vii for more information.

Variables:

Name the independent variable.

Name the dependent variable.

What is the question being investigated?

Say how you might have measured the independent and dependent variables.

Fair tests:

Which things would have been kept the same to make this a fair test?

Table presentation:

Can you see any mistakes or omissions on this table?

Can you suggest another way in which this data could be presented?

Table interpretation:

Which (state independent variable value) in the table has the largest/smallest (state dependent variable)?

How many times has this experiment been repeated?

Why has the experiment been repeated (insert number) times?

Are there any results on this table that look unlikely? Explain your answer to the above.

Conclusions:

What is the relationship between (independent variable) and (dependent variable)?

Can you see a pattern in these results?

Evaluations:

How could more information for this table be obtained? *By altering the range/adding intermediate figures, repeating the investigation (more times).*

1 Harriet wanted to find out how the length of a bone affected its strength. She made model
   bones by making tubes of paper of different lengths and hung an increasing number of
   masses from the middle of each tube until it collapsed.

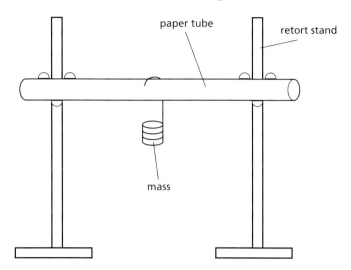

a What things would Harriet need to keep the same to make the test fair?   *(2 marks)*

_____

_____

Level 4

Here are Harriet's results:

Length of tube (cm)	Maximum mass supported by tube (g)
10	720
20	410
30	250
40	180
50	120
60	90

b Describe the pattern shown in these results.   *(1 mark)*

_____

_____

Level 4

c Use the information in the table to predict the maximum mass that could be supported
   by a tube that is:

   i 25 cm long   *(1 mark)*

   _____

   ii 55 cm long.   *(1 mark)*

   _____

Level 5

2 When magnesium powder and hydrochloric acid react they release heat energy, which raises the temperature of the reaction.

Shukkra wanted to find out what volume of hydrochloric acid would produce the highest temperature rise when reacted with 1 g of magnesium powder. She measured out different volumes into five test tubes and added 1 g of magnesium powder to each. She recorded the temperature rise of each tube for the minute after the reaction began.

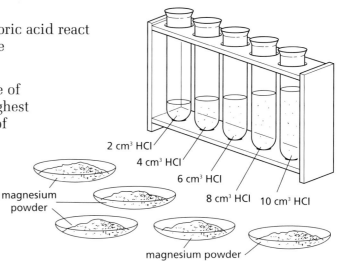

a Suggest the *most suitable* piece of equipment to measure accurately:

   i The volume of acid   *(1 mark)*

_____

Level 4

   ii The mass of magnesium powder   *(1 mark)*

_____

Level 3

   iii The temperature rise of the reaction during the first minute of the reaction. *(1 mark)*

_____

Level 5

The graph below shows the results of the experiment:

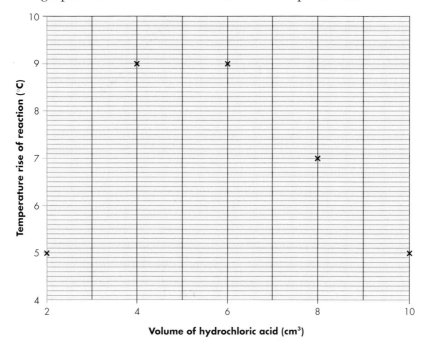

b Between which two volumes of acid does the reaction produce the greatest rise in temperature of the reaction? *(1 mark)*

_____

Level 4

c The precise point of the highest temperature rise is not shown on the graph. How could the data be improved to find this point? *(1 mark)*

_____

_____

_____

Level 5

3 Judy noticed that bubbles rose from the pond weed in her science laboratory. On sunny days she thought that there seemed to be more bubbles than on dull days. Judy decided to plan an investigation into how the brightness of light affected the rate of bubbles produced.

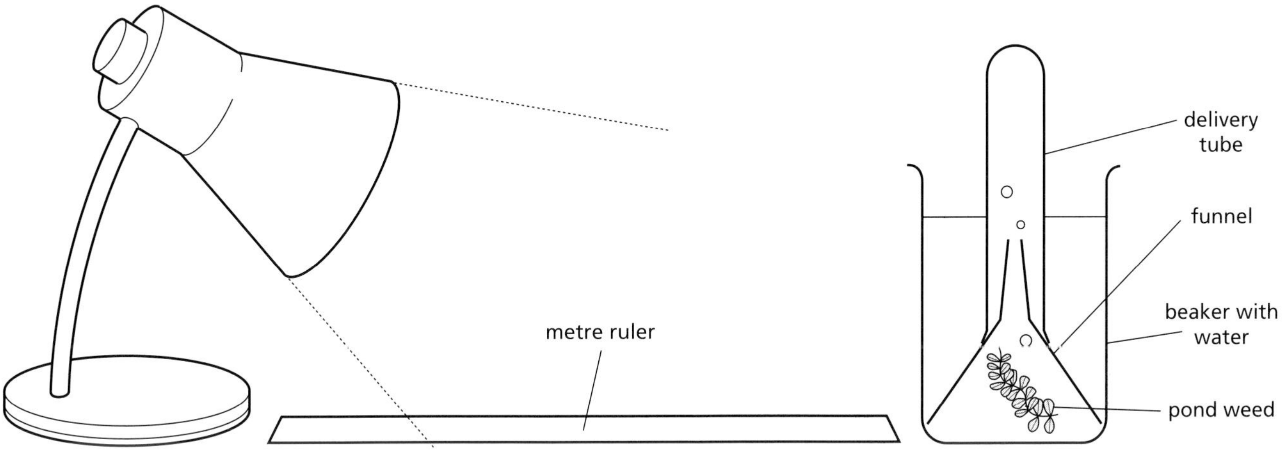

metre ruler

delivery tube

funnel

beaker with water

pond weed

a What variable should Judy change as she carries out her investigation? (the independent variable) *(1 mark)*

_____

Level 4

b What variable should Judy measure as she carries out her investigation? (the dependent variable) *(1 mark)*

_____

Level 4

c Write down two things Judy must keep the same during her investigation. (control variables) *(2 marks)*

_____

_____

Level 4

Here are Judy's results:

Distance of lamp from pond weed (cm)	Number of bubbles per minute
0	76
20	55
40	41
60	31
80	13
100	12

Judy considered the results and wrote:

> The nearer the lamp got to the pond weed the brighter the light it was receiving. The brighter the light was, the greater the rate of bubble production from the pond weed.

d The data that Judy had collected was insufficient for this conclusion to have been made. Explain three reasons why. *(3 marks)*

_____

_____

_____

_____

Level 7

4 A company making fizzy drinks has asked you to investigate what affects how quickly the sugar they use in their drinks dissolves in water. There are a number of variables you can control and some you may wish to alter. Think of one of these variables that you would like to investigate.

a What will you change as you carry out the investigation? (the independent variable) *(1 mark)*

_____

Level 4

Sc1 Skills for Key Stage 3 © Pearson Education Limited 2004

b What will you measure as you carry out the investigation?
(the dependent variable)   *(1 mark)*

_____

Level 4

c Name one thing that you will keep the same to make the test fair.
(control variable)   *(1 mark)*

_____

Level 4

Your teacher has suggested that you should repeat each test five times.

d Why is it a good idea to repeat tests?   *(1 mark)*

_____

_____

Level 5

5 Graham and Maggie were asked by their teacher to carry out some research into the
expansivity of steel. They searched the Internet and found the website of a company that
tested different types of metal for industry. The website contained a graph of test results
for the expansion of steel bars:

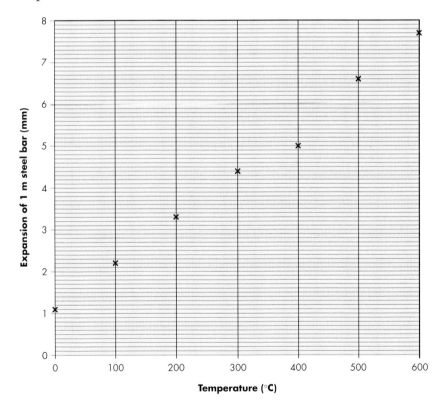

a One of the length readings seems to be incorrect. At which temperature does
this result occur?   *(1 mark)*

_____

Level 6

b Draw a line of best fit on the points of the graph.

(1 mark)

Level 7

c Use the line of best fit to predict a more likely length for the anomalous result.

(1 mark)

Level 7

6 Owain investigated how the voltage of a power supply affected the current flowing through a tungsten filament lamp. He constructed the circuit shown below:

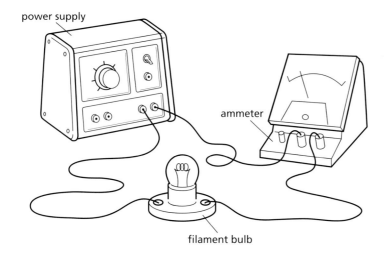

Here are his results:

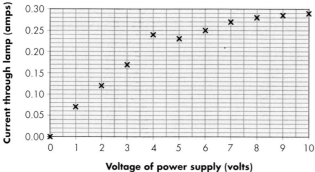

a Describe the pattern found in these results.

(1 mark)

Level 4

b Draw the line of best fit.

(1 mark)

Level 7

Owain thought that one result looked wrong, or anomalous.

c Circle the anomalous result on the graph.   *(1 mark)*

Level 6

d He knew he had read the ammeter correctly. Suggest one reason for this anomalous result.   *(1 mark)*

Level 6

7 Paul and Frances saw an advert on TV claiming that AcidFizz was the best indigestion powder to neutralise stomach acid.

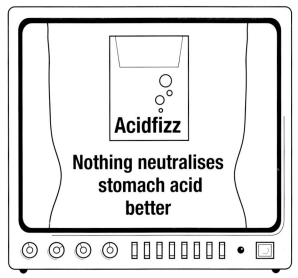

To investigate how effective AcidFizz was compared to two other leading brands, they took three test tubes and added 10 cm³ of dilute hydrochloric acid to each. They then added small masses of each powder to each test tube in turn until the pH of the acid, measured with a pH probe, had reached neutral. They recorded the mass of each powder needed to neutralise the acid.

diluted
hydrochloric
acid

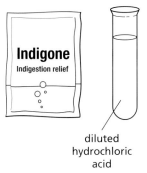

diluted
hydrochloric
acid

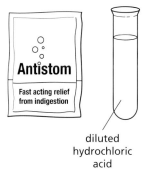

diluted
hydrochloric
acid

a Why was it important that equal volumes of acid were used?   *(1 mark)*

Level 4

b What results would you expect to get if the claims on TV were true? *(1 mark)*

Level 5

Here are their results:

Indigestion powder	Mass of powder required to neutralise acid (g)				
	Test 1	Test 2	Test 3	Test 4	Average
AcidFizz	1.4	1.3	0.7	1.4	1.1
Indigone	1.3	1.4	1.4	1.5	1.4
AntiStom	1.7	1.9	1.8	1.8	1.8

c   These results are insufficient to conclude that AcidFizz was the best powder
    at neutralising acid. Explain why.   *(1 mark*

_____

_____

Level 7

d   What should Paul and Frances do to overcome this problem?   *(1 mark)*

_____

Level 6

8   Amanda and Colin carried out an investigation into how the solubility of copper (II)
    sulphate-5-water crystals changes when the temperature of water increases.

    Here are their results:

Temperature of water (°C)	Mass of copper (II) sulphate-5-water crystals that dissolved (g/100 g water)
10	18.6
20	20.7
30	24.2
40	28.7
50	33.8
60	41.3

a   Plot these results as a graph on the grid provided, making sure that you include:

    i   labelled axes   *(1 mark)*

    ii   an appropriate scale for each axis   *(2 marks)*

    iii clearly plotted points   *(1 mark)*

Level 5

    iv   a line of best fit.   *(1 mark)*

Level 7

Use your line of best fit to answer the following questions:

b What mass of copper (II) sulphate-5-water crystals would dissolve in 100 g of water at:

   i   25 °C   *(1 mark)*

   ii 55 °C?   *(1 mark)*

Level 7

9 Matthew wanted to make a scale model of the Forth rail bridge.

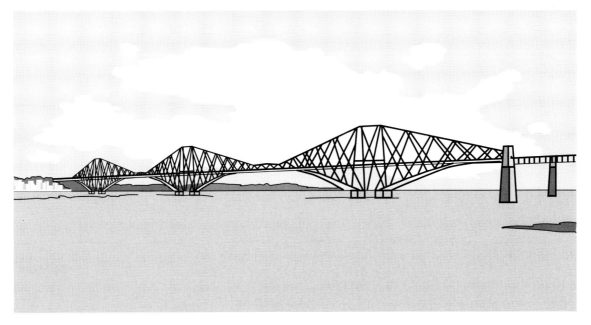

He decided to test rods of three different materials to find out which was the strongest. Each rod was placed between two wooden blocks and an increasing number of 100 g masses hung from them until they snapped.

plastic   wood   PVC

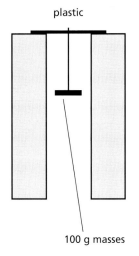 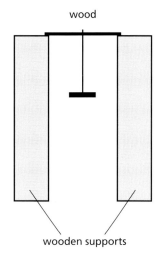 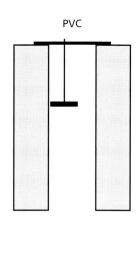

100 g masses   wooden supports

Here are his results

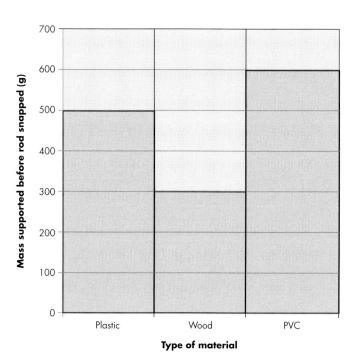

Matthew said that PVC was the strongest material to use.

a   Why should Matthew's conclusion not be trusted?   *(2 marks)*

_____

_____

_____

Level 7

b   How could Matthew improve his investigation to obtain more accurate
information?   *(1 mark)*

_____

Level 6

Sc1 Skills for Key Stage 3 © Pearson Education Limited 2004

10 Ciaran wanted to find out whether it was the length of a spring or its diameter that affected how much it extended when a 500 g mass was hung on it. She set up the following experiment:

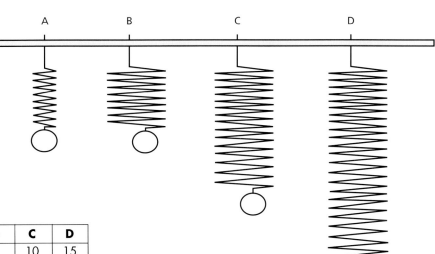

Here are her results:

	A	B	C	D
length (cm)	5	5	10	15
diameter (cm)	1	3	3	3
extension (mm)	25	15	30	45

a Ciaran made three conclusions from these results. In each case decide whether the evidence from the table supports the conclusion, disagrees with the conclusion or is insufficient to make a firm judgement. *(3 marks)*

   i   As the diameter increases, the extension of the spring increases.

   ☐ Supports   ☐ Disagrees   ☐ Insufficient

   ii As the length increases, the extension of the spring decreases.

   ☐ Supports   ☐ Disagrees   ☐ Insufficient

   iii As the length increases, the extension of the spring increases.

   ☐ Supports   ☐ Disagrees   ☐ Insufficient

Level 5

b Using the table, predict the results for a spring with a length of 20 cm and a diameter of 3 cm. *(1 mark)*

Level 6

11 David wanted to find out which fertiliser would help his tomato plants grow the tallest. He took four small tomato plants of the same variety, each measuring 25 cm in height, and fed each with the same amount of four different fertilisers. Each day David watered the plants with 250 cm³ of water. Six weeks later he measured the height of the plants again. Here are his results:

Growlots – 110 cm   WondaFeed – 90 cm

MegaTom – 140 cm   TomaGrow – 115 cm

a Design a table for these figures.

(1 mark)

Level 4

b Which fertiliser appears to have caused the largest increase in height?

(1 mark)

Level 3

c What would David have to do to be sure that the fertiliser chosen for part (b) really does produce the most growth?

(1 mark)

Level 5

12 Lynnette and Sunita dropped a tennis ball from different heights and measured the height of the ball's first bounce.

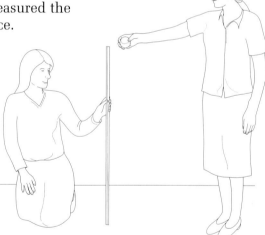

Here are their results:

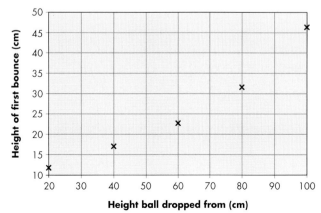

a Name the independent variable.

(1 mark)

_____

Level 4

b Name the dependent variable.

(1 mark)

_____

Level 4

c Describe the pattern you can see between the height the ball was dropped from and the height of its first bounce.

(1 mark)

_____

_____

Level 4

d Draw a line of best fit on the graph.

(1 mark)

Level 7

e Using the line of best fit, predict the height of the ball's first bounce if it was dropped from a height of 70 cm.

(1 mark)

_____

Level 7

13 When hydrochloric acid is added to magnesium, a reaction occurs which gives off hydrogen gas. Simon and Donna wanted to investigate the rate at which hydrogen was produced during this reaction. They set up their apparatus and took readings of the total volume of hydrogen produced when the reaction had finished.

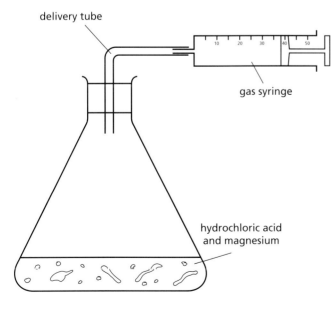

delivery tube

gas syringe

hydrochloric acid and magnesium

Here are their results:

Time (minutes)	Volume of hydrogen produced (cm³)
0	0
1	14
2	25
3	33
4	38
5	40
6	40

a   Plot these results on the graph paper below.   *(1 mark)*

Level 5

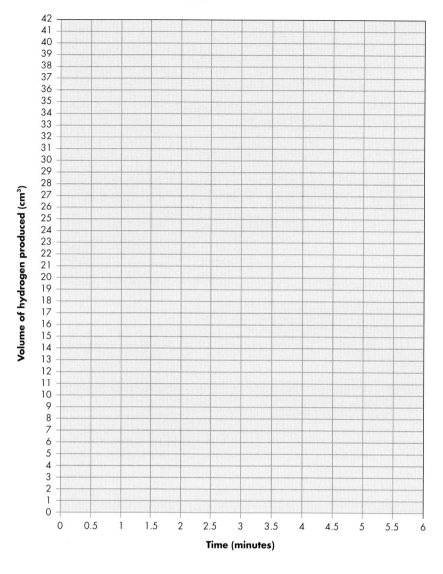

b   Draw on a line of best fit.   *(1 mark)*

Level 7

c   Use your line of best fit to predict the volume of hydrogen that would have been released after 1.5 minutes.   *(1 mark)*

Level 7

14 Valeria investigated how effective bubble wrap was at muffling sound. She measured how far away she could hear an alarm clock ticking and then wrapped the clock with increasing layers of bubble wrap and measured the distance again.

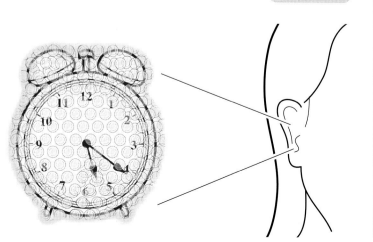

a What piece of equipment should Valeria use to measure her distance from the clock? *(1 mark)*

_____

Level 3

Here are her results:

No bubble wrap - 255 cm

1 layer - 140 cm   3 layers - 35 cm

2 layers - 75 cm   4 layers 10 cm

b Design a table for these results. *(1 mark)*

Level 4

Valeria looked at the results and said that they proved her prediction was correct.

c What was Valeria's prediction? *(1 mark)*

_____

_____

Level 5

15 Anoja investigated how exercise affected her pulse rate. She put on an electronic pulse monitor and waited for her resting pulse rate to be recorded. Some time later she started to run as fast as she could. After a short time she stopped running and sat down again until her pulse rate returned to its resting level. The results are shown on the graph below:

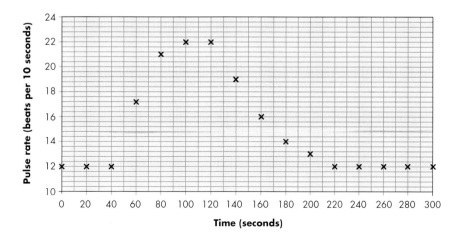

a After how many seconds did Anoja start exercising?

(1 mark)

Level 4

b Explain how you worked out your answer to part (a).

(1 mark)

Level 5

c Between which times was her pulse rate at its highest level?

(1 mark)

Level 4

d How many seconds did it take for Anoja's pulse rate to drop from 132 beats per minute to the lowest point?

(1 mark)

Level 5

Anoja stopped exercising 120 seconds after the start of the experiment.

e Explain why the pulse rate took some time to return to its resting rate.

(2 marks)

Level 6

16 Rob and Joe carried out an investigation into the size of shadows.

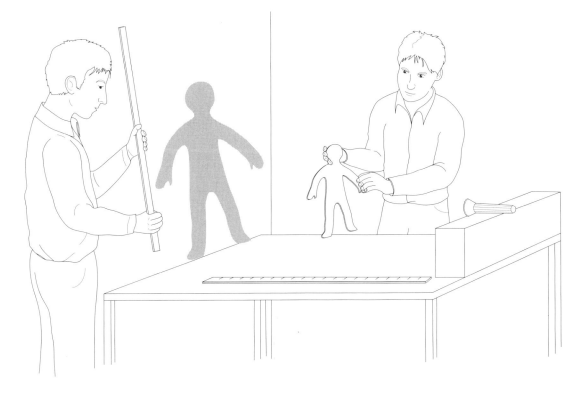

Here are their results:

Distance of card man from torch (cm)	Height of shadow (cm)
20	45
40	28
60	20
80	15
100	13
120	12

a What question were Rob and Joe investigating? Complete the sentence.   *(1 mark)*

   How does the _____ affect the _____?

   Level 5

b Which statements could Joe make from these results?   *(1 mark)*

   i   The further the card man was from the torch, the smaller the height of the shadow.

       ☐ True   ☐ False

   ii The card man changed size as it moved further away from the torch.

       ☐ True   ☐ False

   Level 4

c Rob said that the card man could not be bigger than 12 cm. Explain why.   (1 mark)

   _____

   _____

   Level 6

17 Isabelle and Olivia wanted to find out whether the colour of their T-shirts affected how hot they might feel outside on a sunny day. They took a heater and two tins, one coloured black and the other silver. Each tin was filled with water and placed the same distance from the heater.

The heater was then turned on for 10 minutes. At the end of this time Isabelle and Olivia measured the temperature of the water in each tin.

radiant heater

black tin

silver tin

a Give three things, other than the distance from the heater, that Isabelle and Olivia would have had to keep the same to make the test fair. (control variables)   *(3 marks)*

   _____

   _____

   Level 4

b What piece of equipment could be used to accurately measure the temperature change in the water during the *whole 10 minutes*?   *(1 mark)*

_____

_____

Level 3

At the end of the 10 minutes the temperature of the water in the black tin had risen by 22 °C whilst that of the water in the silver tin had only risen by 8 °C.

c Explain why these results were found.   *(2 marks)*

_____

_____

_____

Level 6

18 Carolyn and Jenny wanted to find out who had the biggest lung capacity. Carolyn took a balloon and inflated it as much as she could with a single blow. She then fully submerged the balloon in a trough of water.

The water that overflowed from the trough was collected and its volume measured.

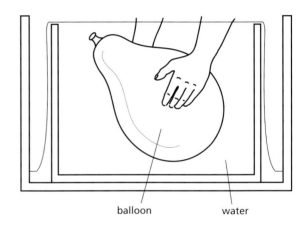

balloon   water

a Name a piece of equipment which could be used to measure the volume of water overflowing.

(1 mark)

Level 3

The trough was then filled up with water again and a different balloon chosen. Jenny then repeated the experiment.

b Suggest two ways in which this investigation was unfair.
(2 marks)

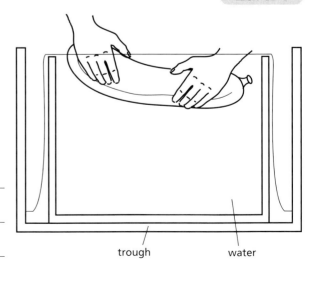

trough   water

_____

_____

_____

_____

Level 4

Here are the results obtained:

Name of person	Volume of water collected (cm³)
Carolyn	1230
Jenny	1110

Carolyn and Jenny's teacher said that their results were not sufficient to make a firm decision about who had the largest lung capacity.

© What would you advise Carolyn and Jenny to do to increase the reliability of these results? *(2 marks)*

_____

_____

Level 5

19 Katie and Roisin dropped ice cubes into water at different temperatures and timed how long the cubes took to melt. Here are their results:

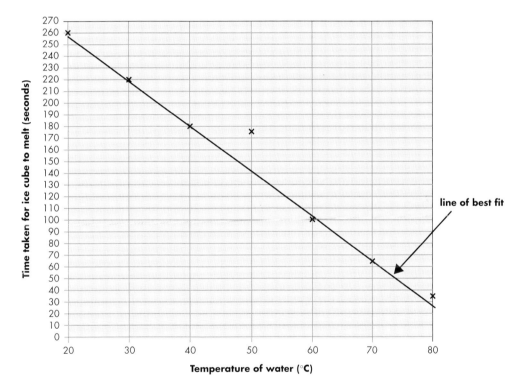

a Describe the pattern that you can see in the results. *(1 mark)*

_____

_____

Level 4

b One of the results looks anomalous. At which temperature does this anomalous result occur? *(1 mark)*

_____

Level 5

c   How would you find out whether this result really was anomalous?   *(1 mark)*

_____

_____

Level 6

d   Explain why you think this result may be anomalous.   *(1 mark)*

_____

_____

Level 6

20 Avril wanted to find out how the temperature of her family's new conservatory changed over the course of one afternoon.

She measured the temperature of the room using a thermometer every hour, noting down the readings on a graph.

a   Avril made sure that she always measured the temperature in the same part of the conservatory. Explain why.   *(1 mark)*

_____

Level 3

Here are Avril's results:

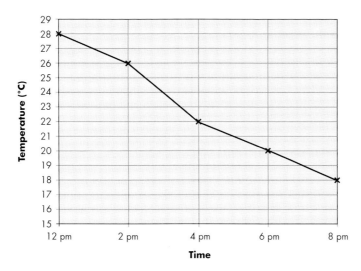

b What pattern can you see in Avril's graph between the time of day and the temperature in the conservatory? *(1 mark)*

_____

Level 4

c Explain why this pattern might have been found. *(1 mark)*

_____

_____

Level 3

Question	Level	Answer	Marks
1a	4	Material of the tubes, thickness or radius of tubes, position where masses attached, positionfizz of retort stands so that there is always the same amount of tube overhanging the edges. *Award 1 mark for each correct answer up to a maximum of 2 marks.*	2 marks
1b	4	As the length of the tube increases, the maximum mass supported by the tube decreases (or the inverse – as the length of the tube decreases, the maximum mass supported by the tube increases). *Or* The longer the tube, the lower the mass supported (or the inverse – the shorter the tube, the greater the mass supported).	1 mark
1c	5	i Accept any figure between 320 and 340 g.	1 mark
1c	5	ii Accept any figure between 100 and 110 g.	1 mark
2a	4	i 10–25 cm³ measuring cylinder or burette.	1 mark
	3	ii Balance / scales.	1 mark
	5	iii Temperature probe (digital thermometer).	1 mark
2b	4	Between 4 and 6 cm³.	1 mark
2c	5	By using intermediate amounts of acid (e.g. 5 cm³).	1 mark
3a	4	Light intensity (the brightness of the light). Accept answers referring to the distance of the lamp from the pond weed.	1 mark
3b	4	The number of bubbles produced per unit time.	1 mark
3c	4	Temperature of the water, amount of pondweed, carbon dioxide concentration in water. *Award 1 mark for each correct suggestion up to a maximum of 2 marks.*	2 marks
3d	7	Only one type of pond weed tested, investigation not repeated to check reliability of results, range of distances of lamps insufficient to show a reliable pattern. *Award 1 mark for each correct suggestion up to a maximum of 3 marks.*	3 marks
4a	4	Mass of sugar / volume of water / temperature of water / amount of stirring. *Award 1 mark for any suitable answer.*	1 mark
4b	4	Time taken for specific mass of sugar to dissolve.	1 mark
4c	4	Any of the key variables not chosen as the independent variable in (a).	1 mark
4d	5	To check the reliability of results. Accept to compare results with each other to check results.	1 mark
5a	6	400 °C	1 mark
5b	7	Award 1 mark for a suitable best straight line ignoring the 400 °C result.	1 mark
5c	7	5.5 mm	1 mark
6a	4	As the voltage of the power pack increases, the current flowing through the bulb increases (or the inverse – as the voltage of the power pack decreases, the current flowing through the bulb decreases). *Or* The higher the voltage, the higher the current (or the inverse – the lower the voltage, the lower the current).	1 mark
6b	7	Best curved line drawn.	1 mark
6c	6	4 volts	1 mark
6d	6	The heating effect of the current / inaccurate setting of the power pack / inconsistent connections between components. *Award 1 mark for any suitable answer.*	1 mark
7a	4	To make the test fair.	1 mark
7b	5	The mass of AcidFizz added should be least.	1 mark

Sc1 Skills for Key Stage 3 © Pearson Education Limited 2004

Question	Level	Answer	Marks
7c	7	Identification of anomalous result at Test 3 of AcidFizz.	1 mark
7d	6	Repeat the test for AcidFizz and use this data for the calculation of the average mass needed to neutralise the acid.	1 mark
8a	5	i *x*-axis: Temperature of water (°C) *y*-axis: Mass of copper (II) sulphate-5-water crystals that could be dissolved (g)	1 mark
	5	ii Award 1 mark for the suitable scaling of each axis, e.g. Temperature – starting at 10 °C and increasing in 10 °C intervals up to 60 °C. Mass of copper (II) sulphate-5-water crystals that could be dissolved – starting at 10 or 15 and increasing in 5 g or 10 g intervals up to 45 g or 50 g.	2 marks
	5	iii Award 1 mark where all points are correctly plotted. Deduct $\frac{1}{2}$ mark for each incorrect plot.	1 mark
	7	iv Best curve drawn in.	1 mark
8b	7	i 22.1 g *Award mark according to intersection on line of best fit.*	1 mark
	7	ii 37.0 g *Award mark according to intersection on line of best fit.*	1 mark
9a	7	The test was not carried out fairly. Not all masses hung from the centre of the rods. Blocks not the same distance apart for all tests / differing amounts of rod overhang and gap between the blocks. *Award 1 mark for a statement that the test was not carried out fairly with one piece of evidence and up to 1 further mark for another piece of evidence linked to the diagram.*	2 marks
9b	6	Using smaller masses.	1 mark
10a	5	i Insufficient (only two results are not sufficient data to form a pattern).	1 mark
	5	ii disagrees	1 mark
	5	iii supports	1 mark
10b	6	60 mm	1 mark
11a	4	*table below* *Award 1 mark for all correct.*	1 mark
11b	3	MegaTom	1 mark
11c	5	Accept answers that indicate the need to repeat investigations to be sure of the reliability of the conclusions drawn.	1 mark
12a	4	Height the tennis ball was dropped from.	1 mark
12b	4	Height of the tennis ball's first bounce.	1 mark
12c	4	As the height the tennis ball was dropped from increased, the height of the first bounce increased (or the inverse -– as the height the tennis ball was dropped from decreased, the height of the first bounce decreased). *Or* The higher the tennis ball was dropped from, the higher the first bounce (or the inverse – The lower the tennis ball was dropped from, the lower the first bounce).	1 mark
12d	7	Best curve drawn.	1 mark
12e	7	26 – 28 cm as shown by best curve.	1 mark

Table for 11a:

Fertiliser	Height of tomato plant after two weeks (cm)
Growlots	110
MegaTom	140
WondaFeed	90
TomaGrow	115

Question	Level	Answer	Marks
13a	5	All points plotted correctly.	1 mark
13b	7	Best curve drawn.	1 mark
13c	7	19–21 cm³ – from line of best fit.	1 mark
14a	3	A ruler.	1 mark
14b	4	*(see table below)*	

Number of layers	Distance ticking could be heard from (cm)
0	255
1	140
2	75
3	35
4	10

Award 1 mark for all correct.

Question	Level	Answer	Marks
14c	5	I think that as the number of layers increases the distance at which I will be able to hearing the ticking of the clock will decrease (or the inverse –– I think that as the number of layers decreases the distance at which I will be able to hearing the ticking of the clock will increase). *Or* The more layers there are, the quieter the ticking (or the inverse – the less layers there are, the louder the ticking).	1 mark
15a	4	40–50 seconds	1 mark
15b	5	After 40 seconds on the graph is where the pulse rate begins to rise, and it is probably some time before 60 seconds when it has gone up quite a lot, so a good estimate is between 40 and 50 seconds to allow for some lag effect in the body. *Award 1 mark for a similar answer.*	1 mark
15c	4	100 and 120 seconds.	1 mark
15d	5	100 seconds (between 120 and 220 seconds on the graph).	1 mark
15e	6	The strenuous exercise caused the body to respire anaerobically, producing lactic acid in the muscles. Whilst the lactic acid was present, extra oxygen was needed to be transported from the lungs by the blood to break it down and repay the oxygen debt.	1 mark
16a	5	How does the distance of the card man from the torch affect the height of the shadow?	1 mark
16b	4	i True ii False *Award 1 mark for both (i) and (ii) correct.*	
16c	6	When light from a point source hits an object and casts a shadow onto a parallel surface, the shadow cannot be smaller than the object as light travels in straight lines.	1 mark
17a	4	Equal volume of water in each tin. Same water temperature in each tin at the beginning of the experiment. Tins should be of the same size and shape. Same room conditions (e.g. one may be standing in a draught). Tins placed on same surface. *Award 1 mark each up to a maximum of 3 marks.*	3 marks
17b	3	Thermometer (laboratory or digital)/Temperature probe. *Award 1 mark for naming a piece of equipment that can measure temperature.*	1 mark
17c	6	*Award 1 mark for the comparison between black and silver surfaces in terms of the absorption of radiant heat*: Black surfaces absorb more radiant heat energy than silver surfaces. (Accept 'black surfaces are best at absorbing heat' or 'absorb most heat' or 'silver surfaces are worst at absorbing heat' or 'absorb least heat'. Also accept answers which allude to 'black surfaces reflecting less radiant heat energy than silver surfaces'.)	2 marks

Sc1 Skills for Key Stage 3 © Pearson Education Limited 2004

Question	Level	Answer	Marks
		Award 1 mark for making the link that this energy is then passed through to the water: More heat is transferred to the water in the black tin than the silver tin.	
18a	3	A measuring cylinder.	1 mark
18b	4	Any two from: Balloons are of different shape so one may have been more difficult to inflate than the other. Different amount of hand holding balloons underwater. Balloons may have been made of different materials. Whole balloon not submerged in one case.	2 marks
18c	5	Repeat the test a number of times.	1 mark
		Calculate the average amount of water / lung capacity for each girl.	1 mark
19a	4	As the temperature of the water increased, the time taken for the ice cube to melt decreased (or the inverse – as the temperature of the water decreased, the time taken for the ice cube to melt increased). *Or* The higher the temperature of the water, the faster the ice cube melted (or the inverse -– the lower the temperature of the water, the slower the ice cube melted).	1 mark
19b	5	50 °C	1 mark
19c	6	Repeat the 50 °C measurement again and compare the result.	1 mark
19d	6	As it lies off the line of best fit.	1 mark
20a	3	To ensure that the test was fair.	1 mark
20b	4	As the afternoon progressed the temperature dropped. *Or* The later in the afternoon it got, the lower the temperature of (or the cooler) the room.	1 mark
20c	3	The sun was getting lower in the sky and so less heat was reaching the conservatory. Windows / patio doors had been opened during the afternoon. The sky had become more cloudy. The outside temperature had dropped. *Award 1 mark for any plausible explanation.*	1 mark

SC1 SKILLS
for Key Stage 3

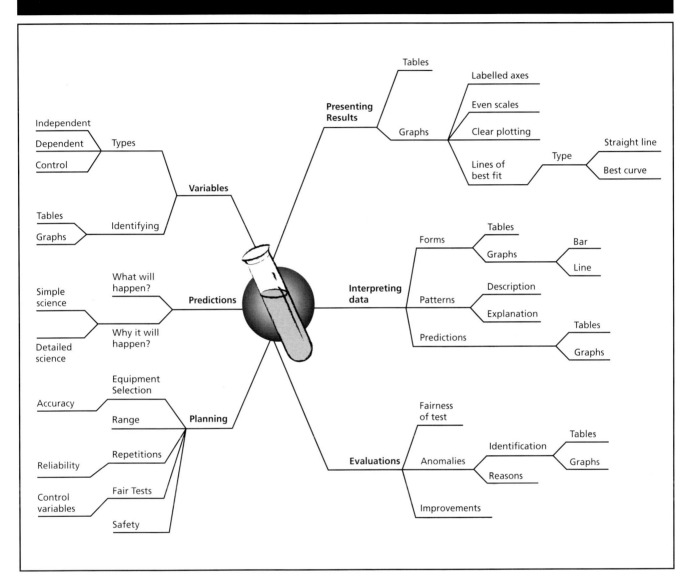

This booklet is designed to help you understand the key features of practical investigations.

Space has been left for you to add your own notes on each section.

Name: ....

VARIABLES

Variables are factors in investigations that effect the results. Every investigation has three different types of variable:

- **Independent variables** – the variable that the investigator chooses to increase or decrease during the course of the investigations.

- **Dependent variables** – variables that change when the independent variable changes. This is what the investigator measures.

- **Control variables** – variables that the investigator keeps the same to make sure that the test is fair. For example:

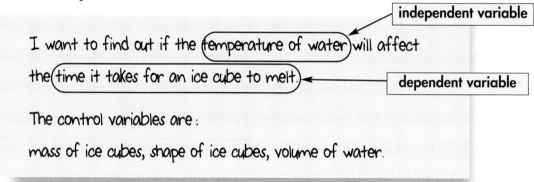

I want to find out if the temperature of water will affect the time it takes for an ice cube to melt.

The control variables are:

mass of ice cubes, shape of ice cubes, volume of water.

You may be asked to identify the different variables from tables and graphs. This is quite easy because they always follow the same pattern:

Tables

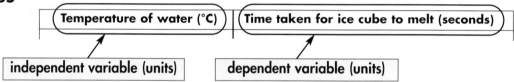

| Temperature of water (°C) | Time taken for ice cube to melt (seconds) |

independent variable (units)   dependent variable (units)

Graphs

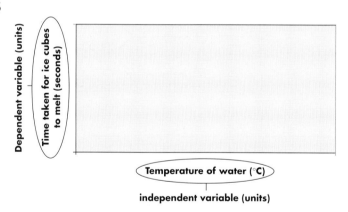

Notes

PREDICTIONS

What will happen when … ?

Saying what

Scientific investigations often involve making predictions (saying what you think will happen) about how changes in the independent variable will affect the dependent variable. The way in which you write this depends on the type of independent variable you are working with. Types of independent variable are:

- **Discontinuous (or discrete) variables** – where the independent variable is not increased but is changed from one form to another. For example:

> I think that when the surface is rough, the shoe will grip more than when the surface is smooth.

In this instance there are only two types of surface being investigated – rough and smooth.

- **Continuous variables** – where the independent variable can be increased. For example:

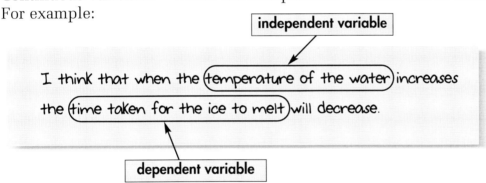

In this instance a whole range of different temperatures is being investigated.

Notes

PREDICTIONS

I think this will happen because ...

Saying why

You should always try to explain why you have made your prediction. If you can, mention how the science you already know has helped you to form your prediction.

Notes

PLANNING INVESTIGATIONS

Your investigative plan should be a clear, step-by-step description of the investigation. This is often helped if you carry out a trial investigation first.

Make sure that you include details on the following things:

Equipment

What equipment will you use?
Try to pick equipment that can ensure the most **precise** measurements or readings.

For example:

a When you require readings of very small changes in temperature, a temperature probe and datalogger give more precise readings than a normal thermometer.

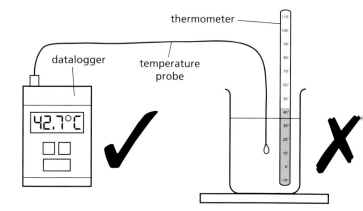

b When measuring volumes of liquid, a measuring cylinder which is just bigger than the volume you want to measure will allow the most precise reading.

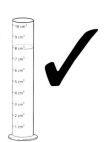

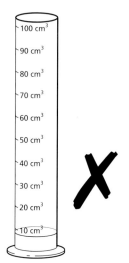

Sc1 Skills for Key Stage 3 © Pearson Education Limited 2004

Range

What **range** of readings will you take? Make sure that your range is wide enough to let you see patterns in your results. For example:

> I will use a range of 20, 30, 40 and 50 °C water for my experiment.

> I will use a range of 21, 22, 23 and 24 °C water for my experiment.

Also try to make the range evenly spread as this will make graph drawing easier.

> I will use a range of 100, 200, 300 and 400 g masses for my investigation.

> I will use a range of 100, 130, 240 and 275 g masses for my investigation.

Repetition

How many times will you repeat the measurements? You should also include reasons why you have chosen this number of repetitions. For example:

> I will repeat my measurements five times so that I can check the reliability of my results.

Fair test

You need to make a list of the variables that you will control to make the test fair and how you will do it. For example:

> How the temperature of water affects how quickly sugar dissolves
>
> To keep my test fair I will keep the following variables the same:
> volume of water,
> mass of sugar,
> number of times the mixture is stirred.

Safety

What **safety** precautions will you need to take?

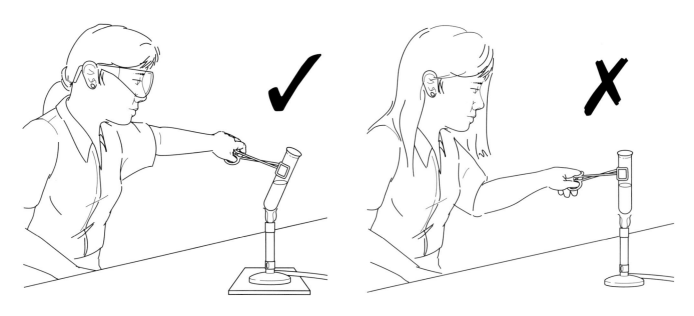

Notes

[blank lined box]

PRESENTING RESULTS

Make sure that all of your results are presented in tables and graphs, as these are the best ways to spot any patterns in the data.

Tables

Use the example shown below to help you to construct your own tables.
Take care to remember the **units**.

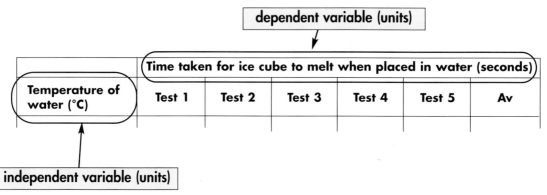

dependent variable (units)

Temperature of water (°C)	Time taken for ice cube to melt when placed in water (seconds)					
	Test 1	Test 2	Test 3	Test 4	Test 5	Av

independent variable (units)

Graphs

Use **bar graphs** for investigations involving discontinuous (or discrete) variables. This is where the independent variable is not increased but is changed from one form to another, for example rough surface and smooth surface. Use line graphs when continuous variables are being used. This is where the independent variable can be increased, for example 10, 20, 30 and 40 °C. Use the examples below to help you to draw your own graphs.

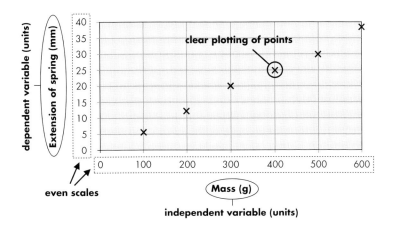

Make sure that your graph has:

• axes *labelled* with the names of the independent and dependent variables and their units

• scales which are *evenly distributed*. For example, 0, 5, 10, 15, 20 or 0, 10, 20, 30, 40, 50

• scales which are *appropriate* for the data being presented

  – For example, if you wanted to plot a range of data from 35 N to 83 N an appropriate scale might be from 30 N to 85 N.

  – If you wanted to make some further predictions outside of this range from your graph an appropriate scale might be from 0 N to 100 N.

• points plotted with a *cross* using a sharp pencil.

Lines of best fit

Once you have plotted your points on a line graph, look to see whether the points form a straight line or a curve. See the examples below:

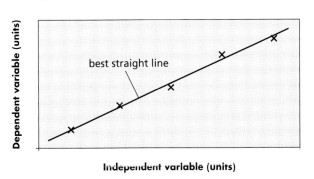

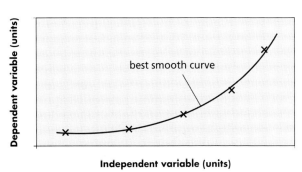

These lines tell the 'story' of the results, revealing the general patterns and trends shown by the data.

Notes

ANOMALOUS RESULTS

Anomalous results are 'strange' results that don't seem to fit in with the general pattern found in the data. Anomalous results suggest that an error may have occurred during part of the investigation, for example misreading measurements, failing to control variables or equipment failure. These anomalies can be easily identified in tables and graphs.

Finding anomalous results in tables

Look at the results in each row of your table. If any appear to be much higher or lower than the others they can be described as anomalous.

Temperature of water (°C)	Time taken for ice cube to melt (seconds)		
	1	2	3
20	210	220	218
30	190	179	183
40	145	(90)	142
50	110	105	107
60	70	67	72

anomalous result

If you find one – ring the value and then repeat the test again, using the new figure to calculate an average.

Finding anomalous results in graphs with lines of best fit

Look at your graph. Are there any points that lie significantly off the line of best fit? If so, ring this point and label it as an anomalous result.

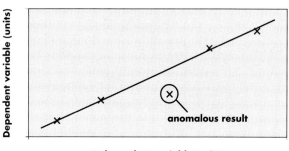

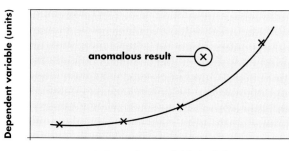

Notes

ANALYSING RESULTS

The reason you present results in graphs is so that you can find answers to your investigative question. This often takes the form of a **pattern**:

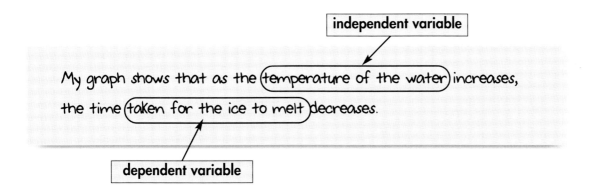

independent variable

My graph shows that as the (temperature of the water) increases, the time (taken for the ice to melt) decreases.

dependent variable

Here are the two most common examples:

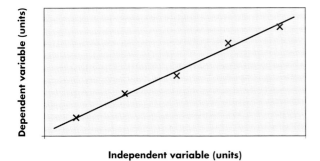

As the independent variable increased, the dependent variable increased.

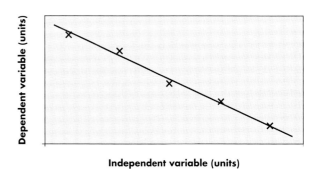

As the independent variable increased, the dependent variable decreased.

Make sure that you compare the findings of your investigation with your predictions. Try to explain these results using your scientific knowledge if possible.

Notes

Making predictions from graphs

You can use graphs to make predictions for values that you have not tested. For example, the graph below shows some plotted results.

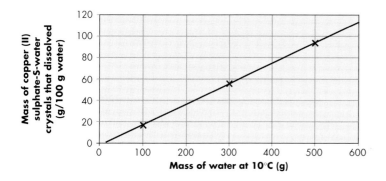

A prediction can be made of the mass of copper (II) sulphate-5-water crystals that dissolved in 200 g water even though it hasn't actually been measured. You do this by drawing on the lines shown below:

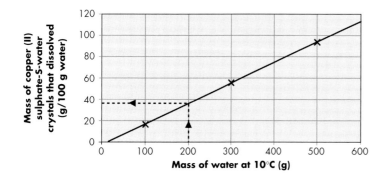

A prediction made within the range of your data is called **interpolation**. A prediction made outside of the range of your data is called **extrapolation**.

EVALUATIONS

At the end of an investigation, look back and consider how well it worked and how fair it was. Think about what kind of questions you should ask:

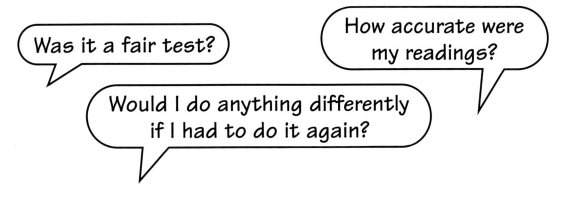

Outline any ways in which you could extend your investigation to gain more evidence for your findings or to examine related matters.

Notes

GENERAL NOTES

Welcome to Sc 1 skills for Key Stage 3 CD-ROM

Running the CD

This CD will run on PC computers only. Your computer should have the following minimum specification.

Windows® 95/98/NT/2000
Pentium® II 166MHz
32 MB of installed RAM
8 x CD-ROM
Monitor with 640 x 480 resolution

The contents of the CD are available in three formats:
* as Acrobat® pdf files
* as Microsoft® Word files
* as Microsoft® PowerPoint files.

You will need Microsoft® Word v7 or later to access Word files.

You will also need Adobe Acrobat® Reader to access the pdf file. A copy of the Reader is included on the CD. Click on the icon and follow the on-screen instructions.

You will also need Microsoft® PowerPoint or PowerPoint viewer to access the Microsoft® PowerPoint files. PowerPoint viewer may be downloaded free from the Microsoft® website.

Licence Agreement: *Sc 1 skills for Key Stage 3 CD-ROM*

Warning:
This is a legally binding agreement between You (the school) and Pearson Education Limited of Edinburgh Gate, Harlow, Essex, CM20 2JE, United Kingdom ('PEL').

By retaining this Licence, any software media or accompanying written materials or carrying out any of the permitted activities on *Sc 1 skills for Key Stage 3 CD-ROM* You are agreeing to be bound by the terms and conditions of this Licence. If You do not agree to the terms and conditions of this Licence, do not continue to use *Sc 1 skills for Key Stage 3 CD-ROM* and promptly return the entire publication (this Licence and all software, written materials, packaging and any other component received with it) with Your sales receipt to Your supplier for a full refund.

Sc 1 skills for Key Stage 3 CD-ROM consists of copyright software and data. The copyright is owned by PEL. You only own the disk on which the software is supplied. If You do not continue to do only what You are allowed to do as contained in this Licence You will be in breach of the Licence and PEL shall have the right to terminate this Licence by written notice and take action to recover from You any damages suffered by PEL as a result of Your breach.

Yes, You can:
1. use *Sc 1 skills for Key Stage 3 CD-ROM* on Your own personal computer as a single individual user;

2. use the *Sc 1 skills for Key Stage 3 CD-ROM* on a school network;

3. modify, print out and copy individual documents from *Sc 1 skills for Key Stage 3 CD-ROM* for classroom use;

No, you cannot:
1. copy *Sc 1 skills for Key Stage 3 CD-ROM* (other than making one copy for back up purposes);

2. alter the software included on *Sc 1 skills for Key Stage 3 CD-ROM*, or in any way reverse engineer, decompile or create a derivative product from the contents of the database or any software included in it;

3. include any software data from *Sc 1 skills for Key Stage 3 CD-ROM* in any other product or software materials;

4. rent, hire, lend or sell *Sc 1 skills for Key Stage 3 CD-ROM*

5. copy any part of the documentation except where specificall indicated otherwise;

6. use the software in any way not specified above without the prior written consent of PEL.

Grant of Licence:
PEL grants You, provided You only do what is allowed under th Yes, You can table above, and do nothing under the No, You cannot table above, a non-exclusive, non-transferable Licence t use *Sc 1 skills for Key Stage 3 CD-ROM*.

Limited Warranty:
PEL warrants that the disk or CD-ROM on which the software is supplied is free from defects in material and workmanship ir normal use for ninety (90) days from the date You receive it. This warranty is limited to You and is not transferable.

This limited warranty is void if any damage has resulted from accident, abuse, misapplication, service or modification by someone other than PEL. In no event shall PEL be liable for ar damages whatsoever arising out of installation of the software, even if advised of the possibility of such damages. PEL will nc be liable for any loss or damage of any nature suffered by any party as a result of reliance upon or reproduction of or any errors in the content of the publication.

PEL does not warrant that the functions of the software meet Your requirements or that the media is compatible with any computer system on which it is used or that the operation of th software will be unlimited or error free. You assume responsibility for selecting the software to achieve Your intende results and for the installation of, the use of and the results obtained from the software.

PEL shall not be liable for any loss or damage of any kind (except for personal injury or death) arising from the use of *Sc 1 skills for Key Stage 3 CD-ROM* or from errors, deficienci or faults therein, whether such loss or damage is caused by negligence or otherwise.

The entire liability of PEL and your only remedy shall be replacement free of charge of the components that do not meet this warranty.

No information or advice (oral, written or otherwise) given by PEL or PEL's agents shall create a warranty or in any way increase the scope of this warranty.

To the extent the law permits, PEL disclaims all other war-ranties, either express or implied, including by way of example and not limitation, warranties of merchantability and fitness fo a particular purpose in respect of *Sc 1 skills for Key Stage 3 CD-ROM*.

Governing Law:
This Licence will be governed and construed in accordance wi English law.